Dae*licious!*
Recipes for vibrant living

Dr. Daemon Jones

Healthydaes
Naturopathic Medical Center

Daelicious! Recipes for Vibrant Living, 2nd Edition

Healthydaes Naturopathic Medical Center
www.healthydaes.com
info@healthydaes.com

———————————————

ISBN: 978-1-60530-690-2

———————————————

The information in this book has been prepared to encourage
people to be thoughtful about what they put into their bodies. It
is intended to help people recognize that food is medicine. This
book does not take the place of a consultation with a qualified
naturopathic or other physician for diagnosis or medical treatment
of any disease.

Cover photography: Demetrius Robinson, Marsha Tomassi
Cover & book design: Sophora Studios

Manufactured in the United States of America
10 9 8 7 6 5 4 3 2

To all those people who want to eat well and are afraid it's just not going to taste good.

Surprise!

Acknowledgements

I want to give special acknowledgements to:

- My family, who support and encourage me to live out my dreams – always!

- My foodies! Thank you for sacrificing your taste buds to try my recipes: Jennifer Benn, Lisa Cardwell, Jennifer Cook, Lisa Copeland, Daryl Jones, DeBorah Posey, Theresa Stone, and Nicole Stevenson.

- All my friends, mentors and patients who supported this book from conception to creation. You know who you are. I love you!

- Smith Farm Center for Healing and the Arts and its staff -- Michelle Clermont, Shanti Norris, Greg Finch, Myrtle Washington, Carole O'Toole and Darien Reece. They trusted my love and knowledge of food and allowed me to teach it to others. They helped me to be better and better and better all the time.

- The Center for Mind-Body Medicine, especially Susan Lord and Jo Cooper, for seeing my spark and giving me the opportunity to become a faculty member for the Food As Medicine program and the Director of Community Nutrition for the Blaustein Nutrition Group.

- Cindy Klein for formatting assistance, Klára Royal for her expert proofreading, and Demetrius Robinson and Marsha Tomassi for their skilled photography.

And an extra special thanks to my editor, Jo Cooper, who helped me bring my vision into reality. There is no greater supporter than my family.

Table of Contents

Forward

The twenty-first century has ushered in a refreshing trend toward healthy eating for healthy living. The way we eat has a lot to do with our cultural backgrounds, of course. But despite cultural differences, the American diet has been known for its rich fried foods, cheeses, processed foods, and sugary deserts. Because we have known these tastes since childhood, consuming them is habit that can be difficult to change. However, in this uplifting book, Dr. Daemon Jones offers a wealth of information and resources to help anyone who longs to break away from destructive eating habits and join the twenty-first century drive towards eating well and feeling rejuvenated.

A number of features of modern life have contributed to less-than-healthy eating habits. For instance, with the work schedules of heads of families or those responsible for meal preparation, fast foods which take little to no time to prepare are an attractive alternative. Because of the convenience of frozen dinners, some families and individuals have not known the taste of fresh foods for a long time. There is also the element of time. Our increasingly busy lives have caused us to eat in a hurry, to eat on the go, and to eat later and later in the day, well past the recommended 6:00 pm dinner hour. And let us not forget the comfort foods that get us through emotional dramas!

With all these factors, is it any wonder that obesity is on the rise? We are an obese nation, from children to adults. So widespread has obesity become over the last several decades that some of our city mayors have begun public exercise programs to assist residents in weight loss—one element in maintaining a balance of body, mind and spirit. Maintaining this balance means physical exercise, training the mind to explore inspirational materials for both the intellect and the emotions, and relating daily to the divine nature born within us by the creative Power of the Universe. Once we change the direction of the imbalanced journey that results in undesirable outcomes such as obesity, we will begin to realize the benefits of a new body which is already a self-healer, desiring only our help in maintaining it.

Daemon Jones, a young, vibrant medical professional, is showing us the way to healthy living. Her book focuses on healthy, whole foods, and the powerful benefits of thoroughly changing our current eating habits if our body is under attack with illnesses that cause us pain and sorrow. She focuses on diabetes, which is a leading cause of illness in our communities, inflammation, cancer, obesity, high blood pressure and other common ills of our times.

What this book has to say about eating is so necessary. Dr. Jones is sensitive to those who may be at the poverty level or slightly above it and may not have the resources to shop in grocery stores offering organic meats, vegetables, fruits, and other items common to the kitchen at prices they cannot afford. I especially liked this chapter because it offers all of us a way to reach the comfort zone of eating good foods, no matter what our economic status.

There is also a useful section on creating a pantry. For many senior citizens, this section will be a pleasant reminder of bygone days when the pantry was the focal point of the kitchen, bursting over with home-grown vegetables and fruits cooked and canned in the summer in preparation for winter. What a beautiful sight to behold those pantries were! The colors of soup mixtures, preserves, and a variety of veggies on the shelf, waiting to be opened, in specially designed glass jars used for the preservation of varieties of nutritious, precooked foods.

Finally, Dr. Jones demonstrates all of the above ways to develop healthy eating habits by giving us easy-to-prepare recipes that will be pleasing to the palate through ingredients that blend together for our enjoyment. I myself have enjoyed recipes of this kind and found that they did wonders for my body. Admittedly, releasing fried foods, cheeses and dairy products was not an easy task for me until I faced a health challenge that needed to be healed through medicine, a balanced diet, and exercise. I soon learned that with my new organic diet and exercise, the need for medication became less and less. Needless to say my spiritual attunement was in divine order.

My change holistically (spirit, mind and body) came at a time in my life when I could afford a wide variety of health food and herbal remedies. However, I have counseled many individuals and families who were unable to patronize vendors of such products. Even in such situations, through considering what resources were available in the community, such as farmers' markets and co-operatives, and by lifestyle changes such as substituting low-fat, low-sodium home-cooked meals for fast food these individuals and families often found that they could indeed afford the healthy eating lifestyle they previously thought was out of reach for them. With Dr. Jones' book as a resource, those making a change of this kind will find a source of support always close at hand.

I am extremely happy and excited about this publication that gives people of whatever economic level the knowledge they need to have a healthy diet that will help them to reverse their unhealthy lifestyle to one of wellness for a long life of peace, joy, and happiness. The three major religions of the world speak of health in their sacred texts--for Christians, the Bible; for Jews, the Torah; and for Muslims, the Koran. Because we find these themes throughout sacred writings, it is clear that the Power of the Universe has always meant for us to nourish our spirits and our minds with nutritious foods and other natural elements that support the many needs of these complex wonders we call our bodies.

You will find this book well worth reading and experiencing.

Peace,

Reverend Dr. Barbara L. King
Founder-Minister
Hillside International Center
Atlanta, Georgia
November 2007

Introduction

I want people to understand that cooking and eating healthy can and should be a delicious and fun activity to be shared with loved ones, family, friends, and community. Food is beautiful, and should be considered a joy for the eyes, nose, taste buds and tummy. I want Americans to be more connected with their food, especially whole foods, and become more conscious about what they are putting in their mouths. I want them to understand that eating well gives them energy and the ability to achieve their life goals and dreams. Eating poorly takes these things away---something many people don't realize.

Now that I look back, I see how food has always been a passion in my life. My paternal grandparents grew up on farms in North Carolina, so organic food is in my blood. My great aunt used to laugh at the little city girl walking around with bare feet on the farm, picking flowers and tomatoes. My taste buds and love of experimentation must have come from my dad, who has the gift of creating incredibly delicious and fantastic food. At the end of every month, he would make a big pot of succotash – which was whatever was left in the refrigerator – and open the front door and let friends just pour in to chat, eat, and enjoy company. While my mom was not into cooking, she always took me to exotic restaurants, and encouraged me to taste food, enjoy spices, love fragrances, and see the beauty that food has to offer. My mom says that even as a small child I used to add mystery ingredients to her cakes, and that they always tasted better than without my ingredients. What a great life for a child!

As I got older, I gravitated to my friends' parents who could cook extremely well, and asked them to teach me how to make my favorite dishes of theirs. By the time I was a junior in college I was in charge of the kitchen, while my roommates handled other chores. For a time I worked in corporate America and had no time to cook, but I explored as many restaurants as I could. When I became a student in naturopathic medical school and eventually a doctor, I started to play around with recipes to figure out how to make them healthy and tasty at the same time. I realized that many of my patients needed help with changing their diets. They wanted simple recipes that allowed them to stay on the diets I recommended. So I started teaching cooking classes and creating quick and yummy recipes to help them obtain vibrant, energetic lives.

This book has been created to support each of my patients and each of you in achieving your health goals in a delicious way. Thank you for supporting my efforts to create a healthier, whole foods world.

Daemon Donyelle Jones, ND

Recipes for vibrant living

Introduction to Recipes

Food is the fuel you need to live your most vibrant, energetic, passion-filled life! When you eat food with vibrant colors that tastes fresh and makes your taste buds sing, your mind and body can't help but heal and repair itself.

I have organized these recipes the way I think about putting together meals. I like to have at least one serving of protein, whole grains, vegetables or fruit and, on occasion, a sweet thing. Proteins can be plant-based or animal-based. Grains can be served on their own or mixed with vegetables, dried fruits or nuts to add flavor. I love green leafy veggies and try to have them with every meal. A great rule of thumb is to make sure that each meal has lots of color, and vegetables are a fantastic way to do that. Many people like sweets, and fruits are a good way to satisfy that sweet need without resorting to sugar or refined, processed foods.

At the bottom of each recipe is a key that explains which food lifestyles the recipe will support. If you want to find out which food lifestyle might improve a health condition that you are experiencing, you can turn to the **Food Lifestyles** section to read about them.

Food Lifestyle Key

      Anti-Inflammatory

      Blood Sugar Balancing

      Dairy-Free

      Detoxification

Elimination

 Liver Enhancing

 Vegan

 Gluten-Free

 Whole Foods *(all recipes)*

Recipes tend to serve 4, except soups, which serve 8.

Enjoy!

Proteins

Minty Lentil Salad

Lentils are a great source of plant-based protein and soluble fiber, which support improvement of many health conditions.

Dressing ingredients:
1/4 cup extra virgin olive oil
1/4 cup red wine vinegar
4 cloves garlic, minced
1/2 teaspoon ground cumin
1/2 teaspoon sea salt
1/2 teaspoon pepper
Salad ingredients:
3 cups of water
1 cup green lentils
1 cup finely chopped red onion
1 red, yellow or orange bell pepper, diced
1/4 cup chopped fresh mint

1. In a small bowl whisk together olive oil, vinegar, garlic, cumin, salt and pepper.
2. In a saucepan add 3 cups of water and bring to a boil.
3. Rinse the lentils and drain. Add them to the water and reduce heat. Simmer uncovered for 15-20 minutes.
4. Once they are tender, drain and place in a bowl.
5. Add bell pepper and red onions. Gently pour the salad dressing over the lentil mixture.
6. Top with chopped mint.
 *To include this as a part of anti-inflammatory or elimination foodlife style delete the bell pepers from the recipe.

Tomato-Basil Chickpea Salad

Tomato-Basil Chickpea Salad is great by itself or over salad greens. It can also be served in pita pockets as a lunchtime treat. Make sure to drain any extra salad dressing before spooning the salad into pita pockets.

1/4 cup extra virgin olive oil
2 tablespoons white wine vinegar
1 teaspoon sea salt
1/2 teaspoon freshly ground pepper
1 cup cooked chickpeas (may use canned)
3 plum tomatoes (or freshest variety available), chopped
1 cup chopped red onion
1 cup chopped fresh basil

1. In a small bowl combine olive oil, vinegar, salt and pepper.
2. In a large bowl combine the chickpeas, tomatoes and onion.
3. Pour salad dressing over mixture and toss.
4. Top with fresh basil.

Healing Turkey Soup

This soup is particularly good to make whenever you are feeling under the weather and want something nutritious to eat. The broth is easy to digest and will help provide the electrolytes you need to speed your recovery.

1-2 tablespoons extra virgin olive oil
3 yellow onions, large slices
4 carrots, large slices
8 large garlic cloves, crushed
2 cups butternut squash, cubed
3-4 parsnips, large slices
6 cups water
4 cups low-sodium chicken broth
4 skinned and cleaned chicken or turkey legs (with bones)
5 celery stalks, large slices
1 cup dehydrated wild mushrooms
1 tablespoon dried thyme
1 tablespoon dried parsley
1 teaspoon dried sage
4 bay leaves, wrapped in cheesecloth
1 teaspoon freshly ground black pepper
2 whole cloves
1 teaspoon sea salt

1. Preheat oven to 400°F. In a large bowl toss the oil with onions, carrots, 4 cloves of garlic, butternut squash, and parsnips until lightly coated.
2. Arrange the vegetables as flat as possible in a roasting pan. Roast, stirring veggies once, for 30-45 minutes or until golden brown and tender.
3. In a large saucepan or stockpot bring water and chicken broth to a boil. Add chicken or turkey legs, 4 remaining cloves of garlic, celery, dehydrated mushrooms, thyme, parsley, sage, bay leaves, black pepper, cloves, and water. Simmer, stirring occasionally for 30 minutes.
4. Once the vegetables are roasted add them to the pot along with the sea salt and cook for another 20 minutes.
5. Cooking time is about an hour in total. The meat will be in large pieces and you may wish to remove them, cut them into smaller

pieces and return them to the soup before serving.

Spicy Cashew Green Beans

This is a quick recipe that adds some protein-and some pizzazz-to your vegetables. Cashews are a good choice because they have a "cheesy" taste that is appealing to many taste buds.

1/2 pound of green beans, washed and trimmed
2 tablespoons extra virgin olive oil
1/2 cup chopped red onion
1/2 cup raw cashews
Pinch of sea salt to taste
Pinch of black pepper
1 teaspoon paprika
1 teaspoon chopped fresh flat leaf parsley

1. In a 4-quart pan, heat water to a boil and cook the green beans for 3-4 minutes. Drain in a colander and run cold water over the green beans immediately to stop the cooking process.
2. In a frying pan, add olive oil, onions, cashews, salt, pepper and paprika. Cook for 3 minutes on medium heat.
3. Add the green beans and cook for another 2-3 minutes.
4. Sprinkle parsley on top and serve.

Black Bean Chili

This is a hearty recipe for a get together with family and friends. It makes plenty-for 8-10 people-and freezes well, too.

2 tablespoons extra virgin olive oil
1 cup chopped yellow onion
1 cup chopped red bell pepper
2 tablespoons garlic, minced
1 medium zucchini, diced
1 medium eggplant, diced
2 cups corn kernels (fresh or frozen)
5 large portobello mushrooms, cubed
1 tablespoon chili powder
1 tablespoon ground cumin
1 1/4 teaspoons sea salt
Pinch of cayenne pepper, or to taste
4 large tomatoes, peeled, seeded and chopped
3 cups cooked black beans (2 15-ounce cans)
1 (15-ounce) can tomato sauce
1 cup vegetable stock (check label for gluten free)

1. In a large pot, heat the oil over medium-high heat. Add the onions, bell peppers and garlic, and cook about 3 minutes.
2. Add the zucchini, eggplant, corn and mushrooms, and cook, stirring, until soft, about 5-6 minutes.
3. Add the chili powder, cumin, salt and cayenne, and cook about 30 seconds.
4. Add the tomatoes, beans, tomato sauce and vegetable stock and stir well.
5. Bring to a boil. Reduce the heat to medium-low and simmer, stirring occasionally, for about 20 minutes.

Hummus Half-Moon Pies

This makes a delicious lunch or light supper with the Marinated Kale and Carrot Salad, for example, and is a perfect way to create healthy finger food for children. You can hide vegetables inside the tortillas! For young children, cut the half-moons in half. For added flavor, try using red pepper hummus, or red pepper tortillas with regular hummus. These pack well for a school lunch.

4-6 whole wheat tortillas
1 cup hummus
1/2 cup chopped scallions
1/2 cup salsa
1/2 cup minced mushrooms
1/2 cup grated carrots

1. Take one tortilla and add about 1 tablespoon of hummus, spread evenly.
2. Add a teaspoon each of scallions, salsa, mushrooms and carrots and fold in half creating a half moon.
3. On medium heat (with no oil in the pan) place the half moon on the pan to warm for 30-45 seconds. Turn over and heat for another 30 seconds.

Tofu Scramble

Tofu takes on the flavor of whatever it is cooked with. This is a colorful, super simple dish with a curry flavor that can be served as part of breakfast, lunch or a light supper.

1 pound firm tofu
4 cloves garlic, minced
1 cup chopped yellow onion
1 cup chopped bell peppers (red, orange and green)
2 teaspoons extra virgin olive oil
1/2 teaspoon turmeric
1 teaspoon chopped fresh parsley
Sea salt and pepper to taste

1. Remove tofu from the package, place on a paper towel and let drain for a few minutes.
2. Sauté garlic, onion, peppers and oil in a sauté pan for 4 minutes.
3. Crumble the tofu into the pan. Add the spices and cook for another 5 minutes. Serve immediately.

Nut Loaf

This turns out soft on the inside and a little crunchy on the outside. Yum!

2 tablespoons extra virgin olive oil
1 cup chopped yellow onion
4 cloves garlic, chopped
2 small portobello mushrooms, chopped
1 cup vegetable stock (check label to make sure gluten-free)
2 teaspoons arrowroot (or corn starch or flour)
1 cup raw cashews
1 cup raw pecans
1 cup raw Brazil nuts
1 cup raw almonds
2 teaspoons chopped hot or sweet pepper
2 teaspoons white wine vinegar
2 teaspoons dried oregano
1/2 teaspoon sea salt
1 teaspoon black pepper

1. Preheat the oven to 375°F. Oil a loaf pan.
2. In a saucepan over medium heat, add the olive oil, garlic, onions and mushrooms. Cook for 5 minutes, stirring occasionally.
3. Add the arrowroot powder and vegetable broth, stirring until it begins to thicken- about 5-8 minutes. Remove from heat.
4. In food processor or blender, add the nuts, pepper, vinegar, oregano, salt and pepper. Blend until coarse-about 30 seconds.
5. Combine ingredients from the saucepan and blend for 30 seconds.
6. Pour mixture into the loaf pan and bake for 30-40 minutes.

* To include as part of an anti-inflammatory food lifestyle remove hot or sweet peppers.

Black Bean Salsa

A super simple salsa, this dish gets better after a few hours in the fridge to let the flavors mix.

1 1/2 cups cooked black beans (15-ounce can)
1 cup corn kernels (fresh or frozen)
1 teaspoon minced fresh jalapeño pepper (optional)
2 medium tomatoes, diced
1/3 cup chopped fresh cilantro
1/4 cup diced red onion
2 limes, freshly squeezed
1 teaspoon ground cumin
1 teaspoon sea salt
1 teaspoon black pepper

Combine all the ingredients in a large bowl. Cover and chill for at least two hours.

Bok Choy Stir-Fry

Bok choy stir-fry is a wonderfully tasty recipe that is easy and affordable. It has incredible immune boosting properties.

2 teaspoons extra virgin olive oil
1 small yellow onion, diced
3 garlic cloves, crushed
1 inch ginger root, peeled and grated,
 or 1/2 teaspoon ginger powder
1 carrot, thinly sliced
2 cups cooked chickpeas (may use canned)
2 cups baby bok choy, washed and chopped
1 teaspoon of sesame oil

1. In a saucepan on medium heat, add olive oil, onion, garlic and ginger. Cook for 2 minutes.
2. Add the carrots, bok choy and chickpeas and cook for another 5 minutes.
3. Drizzle with sesame oil and serve.

Rosemary Chicken Kabobs

The essence of the rosemary stalks permeates the chicken, creating a wonderful taste with every bite. You can also grill these at a low temperature (to avoid heterocyclic amines, which are cancer causing agents).

1/2 cup lime juice
10 garlic cloves, finely chopped
1/4 teaspoon red pepper flakes
1/2 cup extra virgin olive oil
1/4 cup finely chopped rosemary leaves
10-15 fresh rosemary stalks – which will be used as skewers
1/4 teaspoon sea salt
1/4 teaspoon black pepper
1 pound of raw chicken breasts, cut into cubes

1. Mix the lime juice, garlic, red pepper flakes, oil, chopped rosemary, salt, and pepper in a medium-sized bowl.
2. Add the cubed chicken and mix, making sure the chicken is well coated with the marinade. Refrigerate for 2 hours.
3. Preheat the oven to 350°F.
4. Take the chicken from the marinade and push 3 to 4 cubes onto each rosemary skewer.
5. Bake the chicken for 20 minutes or until it is cooked through.

Salmon in Tomato Sauce

Salmon is high in essential fatty acids so it makes a healthy protein choice. Including tomatoes increases the lycopene, a carotenoid, which has powerful antioxidant properties.

4 3-ounce salmon filets
1 teaspoon dried thyme
1/2 teaspoon sea salt
1 teaspoon black pepper
4 teaspoons extra virgin olive oil - divided into 2 portions
2 tablespoons dried thyme
2 teaspoons turmeric
1 teaspoon black pepper
1/2 teaspoon sea salt
1 small yellow onion, chopped (about 1 cup)
4-6 garlic cloves, minced
1 large portobello mushroom, sliced
1 14-ounce can of diced tomatoes (or 4 tomatoes, diced)

1. Preheat the oven to 325°F.
2. Mix thyme, salt, pepper, and 2 teaspoons of olive oil together and spread mixture over the salmon.
3. Bake for 20 minutes or until tender.
4. Remove from the oven and break into chunks.
5. While the salmon is baking, pour remaining olive oil in a saucepan. Add thyme, turmeric, pepper, salt and chopped onion.
6. Sauté for 5-6 minutes or until onions become translucent.
7. Add garlic, mushrooms and diced tomatoes. Simmer for 10 minutes.
8. Remove from heat and mix with chunks of salmon.

Acorn Squash with Turkey

This is a great recipe to use leftover rice from another meal in. For those of you that have a microwave and want to use it, putting the squash in the microwave for 5-10 minutes will soften it and make it easier to cut.

2 acorn squash
1/4 cup water
2 tablespoons extra virgin olive oil
1 medium onion, diced
2 tablespoons chopped fresh parsley
1-2 bay leaves
1/2 teaspoon sea salt
1/2 teaspoon black pepper
2-3 garlic cloves, minced
1/8 teaspoon allspice
1/2 pound of lean organic ground turkey
1 1/2 cups cooked brown rice

1. Preheat the oven to 325°F.
2. Cut the acorn squash into halves and remove the seeds.
3. Pour ¼ cup of water into a baking dish and place squash cut-side down. Bake for 45 minutes or until tender.
4. Remove the squash from the baking dish and pierce with a fork in several places. Let cool slightly while preparing the filling.
5. In a large saucepan, warm oil over medium heat. Add onion, parsley, bay leaves, salt, pepper, garlic and allspice and sauté for about 2 minutes.
6. To the pan, add ground turkey and cook until brown--about 10 minutes.
7. Remove bay leaves
8. Drain the meat and add brown rice.
9. Stuff squash with mixture and bake for 15 minutes.

Salmon with Fresh Herbs

Fresh herbs taste completely different than dried herbs. I got hooked on fresh herbs when one of my patients gave me a few and told me to leave them on my kitchen window and pinch them off as I needed them. Wow! Cost effective, too.

2 tablespoons chopped fresh parsley
2 tablespoons chopped fresh dill
1/4 cup fresh chopped chives
6 cloves garlic, minced
2 teaspoons extra virgin olive oil
2 tablespoons rice wine vinegar
¼ teaspoon sea salt
¼ teaspoon black pepper
4 3-ounce pieces of fresh salmon

1. Preheat the oven to 375°F.
2. Add all of the ingredients except the salmon to a bowl and mix.
3. Cut slits in the salmon and rub the spice mixture inside and on the salmon
4. Marinate for 1 hour if possible.
5. Bake uncovered for 12-15 minutes or until fully cooked. You should be able to easily flake it apart with a fork.

Chicken Lettuce Wraps

I developed this as a novel way to use leftover chicken. I recommend the salad dressings below because they have great flavor and no hidden sugars or high fructose corn syrup. Healthy fast food!

6-8 leaves (keep intact) of red leaf, green leaf or butter lettuce, washed and patted dry
1 cup of leftover chicken, pulled apart
1/4 cup finely chopped red onion
1/4 cup shredded red cabbage
1/4 cup shredded carrots
1/2 cup diagonally diced asparagus
1/2 cup mandarin oranges
1 tablespoon Annie's Naturals Shitake & Sesame Vinaigrette or Tuscany Italian Dressing

1. The lettuce leaf will serve as the base for your wrap. Add pieces of the chicken, red onions, cabbage, carrots, asparagus and mandarin oranges.
2. Drizzle the salad dressing over the chicken, vegetables and fruit.
3. Roll the lettuce like a cigar, and repeat with the remaining leaves.

* To include in the anti-inflammatory lifestyle remove oranges.

Honey Mustard Salmon

This is an easy recipe that takes only a few minutes but is loaded with good essential fatty acids.

3 cloves of garlic, diced
1 tablespoon mustard
2 teaspoons extra virgin olive oil
1/2 teaspoon honey
1/2 teaspoon chopped dill
1/4 cup chopped scallions
4 3-ounce pieces of salmon
Pinch of sea salt
Pinch of fresh ground pepper

1. Preheat the oven to 350°F.
2. Blend garlic, mustard, oil, honey, dill, scallion, salt and pepper into a glaze. Spread over salmon.
3. Marinate salmon for at least 30 minutes.
4. Bake 12-15 minutes or until flaky.

Whole Grains

Quick Tabbouleh

You can serve this easy tabbouleh on lettuce, by itself, or in a pita pocket.

1 cup cooked couscous
1 cup cooked chickpeas (may used canned)
1/4 cup chopped fresh parsley
1 tablespoon chopped fresh mint
1/4 cup chopped red onion
1/4 cup chopped roasted red pepper
1/2 cup chopped tomato
1/2 lemon, freshly squeezed
Sea salt and black pepper to taste

1. In a large bowl add couscous, chickpeas, parsley, mint, onion, red pepper and tomato, and mix lightly.
2. Add lemon juice, salt and black pepper to taste. Mix well.

*To make part of a Gluten-Free food lifestyle replace couscous with Quinoa.

Cornbread Dressing

Dressing can be made vegetarian and taste great. It can be used as a complement with poultry or vegetarian meals. Cornbread has more fiber than a white bread dressing.

8 cups cornbread
3 tablespoons unsalted butter or extra virgin olive oil
1 1/2 cups finely chopped onion
3/4 cup finely chopped celery
1/2 cup finely chopped carrots
1 tablespoon dried thyme
1 teaspoon dried sage
1/2 teaspoon sea salt
1 teaspoon black pepper
1 1/2 cups organic vegetable stock

1. Cut cornbread into 1-inch cubes, place on a large baking sheet and let it get "stale" for several hours or overnight. Place in a large mixing bowl and set aside.
2. Preheat oven to 350°F.
3. In a large skillet, heat butter or oil over medium-low heat.
4. Add onion, celery and carrot and cook, stirring frequently, until softened but not browned.
5. Stir in thyme, sage, salt and pepper.
6. Add mixture to cornbread and toss to blend. Slowly pour in stock and toss to moisten.
7. Spread the stuffing in a buttered or oiled 9x15-inch baking dish. Cover and bake for 20 minutes.
8. Uncover and bake for an additional 20 minutes or until the top is crisp and golden.

Wild Rice with Roasted Nuts

Wild rice is an entirely different grain than white or brown rice, with a unique flavor and texture that will provide a special complement to your meals. Since it takes longer to prepare than other rice, I suggest that you make a couple of batches at a time and freeze some, reheating when you need it.

3/4 cup wild rice
1 teaspoon extra virgin olive oil
2 cups organic vegetable stock(read label to make sure gluten free)
1 tablespoon chopped rosemary leaves
3 cloves garlic, chopped
1/2 cup pecans
1 tablespoons flaxseed oil

1. In a saucepan, add wild rice, olive oil, vegetable stock, rosemary and garlic. Bring to a boil, cover and reduce heat, and simmer for 55 minutes.
2. In another saucepan, add pecans and roast on medium heat for about 5 minutes. Constantly stir to prevent burning.
3. Once the rice is fully cooked, add the toasted pecans and flaxseed oil.

Simply Barley

This dish is great served warm or cold and is perfect for a potluck.

1 cup water
2 cups organic vegetable stock
1 cup pearled barley
1 teaspoon extra virgin olive oil
1/2 cup chopped scallions
1/4 cup chopped celery
5-6 button mushrooms, sliced
1/2 teaspoon sea salt
1/4 teaspoon black pepper

1. In a medium saucepan, bring the vegetable stock and water to a boil over high heat.
2. Add the barley. Reduce heat to a simmer, cover and cook until tender-- about 50 minutes.
3. Drain and place in a large bowl.
4. In a medium skillet, heat a few tablespoons of oil, add scallions, and celery and cook until the celery is crisp-tender, 5-6 minutes, stirring occasionally.
5. Add the mushrooms, salt and pepper, and cook about 5 minutes.
6. Stir the cooked vegetables into the barley. Mix well.

Nutty Rice with Mushrooms

This rice mixture is used as a supplement to your meal. It is best when served with vegetables or protein with a nice sauce to give you more fiber and protein.

2 1/2 cups of water
1 cup long grain brown rice
2 tablespoons sunflower oil
1/2 cup chopped onion
3 cups sliced mushrooms
1/2 cup hazelnuts
1/2 cup pecans
1/2 cup almonds
1/2 teaspoon sea salt
1/2 teaspoon black pepper
Pinch of cayenne pepper
4 tablespoons chopped fresh flat leaf parley

1. Add rice to boiling water and cook for 35-40 minutes or until tender.
2. Drain, rinse with cold water and let water evaporate for a few minutes.
3. Heat 2 tablespoons of oil in wok or big pan. Add onions and mushrooms and cook for 4 minutes.
4. Add hazelnuts, pecans, almonds and stir-fry for 2 minutes.
5 Mix rice salt, pepper, cayenne pepper and parsley and serve.

Wilted Salad with Quinoa

This is a great late summer recipe. Both the quinoa and chickpeas are good sources of protein and fiber.

1 cup organic vegetable broth (read label to make sure gluten free)
1/2 cup quinoa, rinsed
2 ears of corn or 1/2 cup corn kernels (fresh or frozen)
1/2 cup chopped snap peas
1/2 cup chopped red or green bell pepper
1/2 cup cherry tomatoes, halved
1 cup finely chopped fresh basil
1/2 teaspoon sea salt
1/2 teaspoon black pepper
1 cup cooked chickpeas (may use canned)
1/4 cup white wine vinegar
2 garlic cloves, minced
1/3 cup extra virgin olive oil
1/2 cup diced scallions

1. In a 4-quart pan, bring vegetable broth to a boil. Add quinoa, reduce to a simmer, cover and cook until water is absorbed, about 20 minutes.
2. Turn off heat. Wait 5 minutes and fluff with a fork.
3. If using fresh corn, heat enough water to cover the corn cobs and add a pinch of salt. Bring to a boil. Drop corn into the water and cook for 8 minutes. Drain. Cut the kernels of the cob and add to a large bowl.
4. Add quinoa to the bowl. Add snap peas, red and green pepper, tomatoes, 2/3 cup of basil (reserve 1/3 cup for the dressing), salt, pepper, chickpeas and white wine vinegar.
5. In a small saucepan, heat the oil, garlic, scallions and remaining 1/3 cup of basil.
6. Sauté for 1 minute. Remove from heat and pour over the salad. Serve.

Brown Rice with Beans

This is a perfect recipe to serve with Mushroom Gravy or Salmon with Tomato Sauce. Adding beans to this recipe adds to the fiber in this meal.

1 cup of long grain brown rice, rinsed
1/2 cup finely chopped onions
3 garlic cloves, minced
2 cups vegetable broth (read label to make sure gluten free)
1/2 cup water
1 1/2 cups cooked black beans (1 15-ounce can)

1. Place rice in a large pot and sauté for 3-4 minutes.
2. Add onions, garlic, vegetable broth, and water and bring to a boil.
3. Cover and reduce to a simmer. Cook 30 minutes.
4. Add black beans and cook for another 5 -10 minutes or until water is absorbed.

Butternut Squash with Quinoa

If you can't find quinoa, you can substitute couscous and cook for less time (5 minutes), but the recipe will no longer be gluten free.

1 tablespoon extra virgin olive oil
1/2 cup diced yellow onion
3 cloves of garlic, minced
1 tablespoon minced fresh ginger
3/4 cup golden raisins
2 cups butternut squash, peeled and diced small
1/2 teaspoon sea salt
3 cups water
1 cup quinoa, rinsed
3 tablespoons chopped fresh parsley
1/2 teaspoon grated fresh nutmeg

1. In a large saucepan, heat the oil and add onion, garlic and ginger. Cook for 4 minutes.
2. Add raisins and cook another 2 minutes.
3. Add squash and salt and heat over high heat for 2 minutes.
4. Add water, and bring to a boil for about 10 minutes.
5. Reduce heat to a simmer and cook uncovered for 25 minutes or until squash is tender.
6. Once the squash is tender, stir in quinoa, parsley and nutmeg.
7. Cover and cook for another 10 minutes or until water is absorbed and quinoa is done.
8. Remove from heat and fluff the quinoa.

Whole Wheat Pasta Medley

For those people who have not been introduced to whole wheat pasta it has more fiber than white flour pasta and can be used interchangeably in any pasta recipe.

1 cup whole wheat pasta
2 tablespoons extra virgin olive oil
8 garlic cloves, minced
1/2 cup chopped shallots
1/2 teaspoon sea salt or more to taste
1 teaspoon black pepper or more to taste
3/4 cup chopped carrots
3/4 cup chopped asparagus
3/4 cup chopped zucchini or summer squash
3/4 cup chopped fresh parsley
1 fresh lemon, squeezed

1. In a 4-quart pan, add water and bring to a boil. Add whole wheat pasta and cook until tender, about 8-11 minutes.
2. Remove from heat, drain and rinse with cold water to stop the cooking process.
3. In a medium sauté pan, add 1 tablespoon of olive oil, garlic, shallots, salt and pepper, and cook for 2 minutes.
4. Add carrots, asparagus and zucchini or summer squash. Cook vegetables for 5 minutes or until tender.
5. Remove from the heat and mix with the remaining olive oil, cooked pasta, lemon juice and fresh parsley.

Cold Vegetables

Two Tomato Salad

This simple salad is best in the summer when tomatoes are at their peak. Sundrop tomatoes taste like candy and add a wonderful element to this recipe if you can find them. To make it vegan, leave out the mozzarella.

Dressing ingredients:
1 cup fresh basil leaves
2 tablespoons extra virgin olive oil
1 clove garlic
Pinch of sea salt
1/4 cup pine nuts
Salad ingredients:
2 cups of lettuce leaves, torn
1/2 cup chopped sundrop tomatoes
1/2 cup chopped cherry tomatoes
1/2 cup chopped cucumbers
2 tablespoons water
1 cup fresh mozzarella cut into cubes (optional)

1. In a blender combine basil, oil, garlic, salt and pine nuts into a dressing. Blend for about 45 seconds.
2. Tear lettuce leaves into bite size pieces and arrange on the serving plate. Add the tomatoes and cucumbers and fresh mozzarella, if using, in the center of the plate.
3. Pour the dressing over the salad and serve.

* To make dairy free delete mozzarella from the recipe.

Orange Rosemary Salad

This is a nice blend of spices and fruit. The jicama is a wonderful starchy sweet vegetable that adds wonder to this salad. If you cannot find jicama you can use apples as a substitute.

Dressing ingredients:
1/4 cup extra virgin olive oil
1/4 cup juice - Clementine, tangerine or sweet orange
1/2 teaspoon chopped rosemary leaves
1/8 teaspoon sea salt
1/8 teaspoon black pepper
1/8 teaspoon paprika
1/4 teaspoon ground mustard
1 tablespoon red wine vinegar
Salad ingredients:
2 cups mixed salad greens
1 Clementine, tangerine or sweet orange, sectioned and chopped
1 cup chopped jicama
1 cup chopped pecans

1. In a small bowl whisk oil, juice, rosemary, salt, pepper, paprika, mustard and vinegar together.
2. In a large bowl add, salad greens, Clementines, jicama, and pecans.
3. Sprinkle with salad dressing and toss lightly.

Citrus Berry Salad Dressing

This light salad dressing is perfect over any fruit or citrus salad. It would also make a great marinade for fish.

6 fresh strawberries
1/2 fresh Clementine or 1/4 cup of canned Clementine pieces
1/4 cup of safflower oil
1/2 teaspoon of ground ginger
A few pieces of crystallized ginger (optional)
2 tablespoons rice wine vinegar
2 cups mixed field greens, arugula or endive leaves

1. In a food processor or blender puree the Clementines and strawberries for about 5-10 seconds.
2. Add the oil, ground ginger and rice wine vinegar and mix for another 10 seconds.
3. Pour over the salad greens.
4. If you are adding the crystallized ginger, dice into small pieces and add after you have tossed the salad.

Fruity Fall Field Salad

This recipe is a good way of getting your family to eat salad!
Combining apples and walnuts changes up salad from boring to
exciting.

2 tablespoons extra virgin olive oil
2 teaspoons lemon juice
1 teaspoon lemon zest
2 teaspoons walnut oil
2 tablespoons chopped dill
Pinch of sea salt to taste
2 Granny Smith apples, sliced
1/2 cup chopped walnuts
2 cups mixed salad greens

1. In a small bowl whisk olive oil, lemon juice, zest, walnut oil, dill
   and sea salt into a dressing.
2. In a large bowl add salad greens, chopped walnuts and sliced
   apples.
3. Pour salad dressing and toss.

Cranberry Pecan Salad

This is a beautiful salad for the holiday season. Toasting the pecans gives them a deeper flavor.

1/4 cup extra virgin olive oil
2 tablespoon rice vinegar
2 tablespoon honey
1/4 teaspoon sea salt
2 cups spinach leaves
1/2 cup thinly sliced red onion
1/2 cup dried cranberries
1/2 cup raw pecans

1. In a small bowl mix olive oil, rice vinegar, honey, and salt into a dressing.
2. Place pecans in a saucepan over medium high heat for 5 minutes to toast, stirring from time to time.
3. Remove pecans from heat and in a big bowl mix with the spinach, red onions and cranberries.
4. Pour salad dressing and serve.

Fresh and Fruity Salad

The mint in this dressing gives the salad a refreshing taste. It tastes sweeter than most desserts! This makes a hefty portion, so consider halving the recipe or pureeing and freezing the leftovers for a high fiber popsicle that kids love.

2 tablespoons chopped fresh mint
1 tablespoon lemon zest
1 tablespoon lime zest
Juice of 1 orange
Juice of 1 lemon
Juice of 1 lime
1/4 cup turbinado sugar
1 cup fresh raspberries
2 peaches, cut into chunks
2 kiwis, cut into chunks
1 Clementine or tangerine, peeled and broken into wedges
1 cup strawberries, cut into chunks
1 cup blueberries
1 cup pineapple chunks

1. In a small bowl, whisk the fresh mint, lime zest, lemon zest, lemon juice, orange juice, lime juice and turbinado sugar into a dressing.
2. In a large bowl mix together raspberries, peaches, kiwis, Clementines, strawberries, blueberries and pineapple.
3. Pour the dressing over the fruit and refrigerate one hour or until ready to serve.

Strawberry Spinach Crunch

I love this salad. It is a great sweet salad that contains loads of vitamin C. The walnuts give it a nice crunch.

1/4 cup safflower oil
1 tablespoon red wine vinegar
1 teaspoons honey
1/4 teaspoon ground ginger
1 cup fresh strawberries, chopped
2 cups spinach, rinsed and dried
1/2 cup chopped walnuts
1/2 cup finely chopped red onions

1. In a small bowl whisk oil, vinegar, honey, and ginger until well mixed into a dressing.
2. Put field greens in a big bowl and top with strawberries, walnuts and red onions.
3. Pour dressing over mixture and toss to combine.

Marinated Kale and Carrot Salad

This is a new twist on kale because it is not cooked. The acid from the lemon and orange juice actually soften and sweeten the kale. You will be so surprised at how much you enjoy this. You can remove the tomatoes to make this work for the anti-inflammatory lifestyle.

1 bunch fresh kale
3/4 cup extra virgin olive oil
1/2 cup lemon juice
1/2 cup orange juice
1 teaspoon of sea salt
1 medium tomato, diced (optional)
1/2 cup grated carrots
1/4 cup thinly sliced mushrooms
1/8 teaspoon cayenne pepper
1 clove garlic, crushed
1/2 teaspoon oregano
1/2 teaspoon thyme
1/2 teaspoon rosemary

1. Wash the kale leaves and tear them into bite-sized pieces, removing the tough stems.
2. Add the olive oil, lemon juice, orange juice and salt. Stir well to make sure you tenderize the leaves.
3. Add tomatoes, carrots, mushroom, cayenne pepper, garlic, oregano, thyme, rosemary.
4. Let rest for 30 minutes before serving.

*To make anti-inflammatory increase lemon juice to 3/4 cups. Delete orange juice and tomatoes. Add 1/2 chopped avocado to increase taste.

Super Simple Guacamole

This simple guacamole is great because avocados are a wonderful source of good fat. It can be used as a snack or a topping for salads, soups, anything with black beans, or poultry.

2 ripe avocadoes, peeled
Juice of 1 lime
1/4 cup diced onion
1 garlic cloves, minced
1/8 teaspoon cumin
1/4 teaspoon sea salt
1/4 cup chopped fresh cilantro
3 fresh red chilies, diced (optional)
1/2 cup chopped tomatoes

1. Mash the avocados in a bowl.
2. Add lime juice, onion, garlic, cumin, salt, cilantro and chilies. Mix well.
3. Gently mix in the tomatoes.

* To make anti-inflammatory or elimination delete tomatoes.

Cranberry Relish

If this is the first time you are cooking cranberry sauce you want to make sure the temperature is not too high because otherwise as the cranberries 'pop' they will splatter and make a mess on the stove top and your clothes.

2 cups cranberries
1/2 cups turbinado sugar
1/2 cups water
1/2 cup orange juice
1/2 cup orange slices, seeded

1. In a large skillet over medium heat combine the cranberries, sugar, water, and orange juice.
2. Cook for about 10 minutes.
3. The cranberries will start to 'pop' and the liquid will congeal. The longer you cook it the thicker it will be become. I suggest another 5-10 minutes.
4. Remove from heat and add orange slices for texture and flavor.

Cranberry Relish Plus

Outstanding flavor is what makes this a great dish to spice up any meal. Persimmons are generally available in the stores and farmers' markets in the fall. They can be frozen for up to 6 months.

1 cup fresh cranberries
1/4 cup orange juice
1/4 cup water
1/2 cup turbinado sugar
1 persimmon, chopped or diced
1/4 teaspoon ground ginger
1/4 cup walnuts

1. In a 4-quart pan on medium heat add cranberries, orange juice, water and sugar and simmer for 10 minutes.
2. The cranberries will start to 'pop', letting you know you are ready for the next ingredients.
3. Add the persimmon and ginger. Cook for another 10 minutes.
4. Turn off heat, add walnuts, and let cool for 30 minutes.

Warm Vegetables

Very Veggie Udon Soup

I love soups! This one has so many immune-boosting ingredients it can serve as a light meal on a chilly fall or winter day. Buckwheat is a different grain than wheat so this is a delicious soup for everyone, including people with wheat sensitivities.

Strips of cheese cloth and string
2 tablespoons fresh ginger, peeled and sliced
4-5 cloves garlic, crushed
5 cups vegetable broth
2 teaspoons extra virgin olive oil
1 3/4 cups (4 ounces)shiitake or oyster mushrooms, stemmed and sliced
1 cup sliced red onions
1 cup grated carrots
1/4 teaspoon crushed red pepper, or to taste
1 small bok choy, sliced
4 ounces buckwheat udon noodles
1 teaspoon toasted sesame oil
Rice vinegar to taste
2 teaspoons Bragg Liquid Aminos or soy sauce

Garnish:
1/4 cup chopped scallions
3 teaspoons sesame seeds
1/2 cup bean sprouts

1. Wrap the ginger and garlic in cheese cloth and tie together with string. Place this in a stock pot with broth and bring to a gentle boil.
2. Simmer for 12-15 minutes. Remove cheese cloth with ginger and garlic. (If you don't have cheese cloth just strain the ginger and garlic out of the stock.)
3. Add noodles to the stock and cook on low heat for about 8 minutes.
4. In a saucepan add oil, mushrooms, red onions, carrots and crushed red pepper and cook for about 3 minutes.
5. Add bok choy and cook another 2 minutes.
6. Add the mushroom mixture to the stock pot. Simmer for 3 minutes.

7. Add sesame oil and vinegar and Bragg Liquid Aminos to taste.
8. Garnish with scallions, sesame seeds and sprouts.

Basic Veggie Stock

The nice part about making stock is you can use all the parts of the vegetables, throw in roots, stems and all. This simple broth is tasty and freezes well. Consider making batches and freezing it in 1-cup portions.

2 tablespoons extra virgin olive oil
1 cup yellow onion
2 cups zucchini
1 cup carrots
1 1/3 cups celery
1 potato
1 cup dried mushrooms (optional)
1 cup parsley
8 garlic cloves
2 bay leaves
1/2 teaspoon dried thyme
1/2 teaspoon sage
1 cup scallions
1 teaspoon peppercorn
1 teaspoon sea salt
6 cups water

1. Coarsely chop the vegetables.
2. In a large soup pot add olive oil and sauté all the vegetables for 5-10 minutes.
3. Cover the vegetables with water and bring to a boil.
4. Simmer for 45 minutes.
3. Strain the vegetables.

Comforting Carrot Soup

This spicy root vegetable soup goes well with a winter salad with dried cranberries or raisins. The jalapeño gives it a kick, and the fresh dill gives it a smooth finish.

2 tablespoons olive oil
1/2 jalapeño pepper, seeded and chopped (for more of a kick, keep the seeds)
5-6 carrots, sliced
1 yellow onion, sliced
1/2 teaspoon thyme
1/8 teaspoon nutmeg
1/4 teaspoon pepper
1 bay leaf
2 cups vegetable stock
2 cups rice milk or other milk alternative
1 tablespoon dill

1. Place olive oil in the pan on medium heat. Add jalapeño, carrots, onions, thyme, nutmeg, pepper and bay leaf.
2. Stir and coat vegetables with seasonings for 1-2 minutes.
3. Add vegetable stock and bring to a boil. Let cook at a slow boil until the vegetables are tender, about 30 minutes.
4. Remove bay leaf and discard.
5. Remove vegetable mixture from the pot and puree with rice milk in the blender or food processor until smooth.
6. Return to the pan and cook until warm.
7. Serve with the dill as a garnish.

Fantastically Fresh Tomato Soup

Fantastically Fresh Tomato Soup is a refreshing light soup best served in the summer when you can have the freshest tomatoes. It is wonderful with a dollop of Super Simple Guacamole on top, p.52

1 tablespoon extra virgin olive oil
6 garlic cloves, crushed
1/2 cup chopped yellow onions
6 yellow tomatoes or plum tomatoes, chopped
2 cups of organic vegetable broth
1 cup corn kernels
1 cup red or yellow bell peppers, chopped
1 jalapeño pepper, chopped
1/2 teaspoon grated lemon zest
1/2 teaspoon sea salt
1/2 teaspoon black pepper
1 teaspoon apple cider vinegar
1 tablespoon chopped fresh basil
1 tablespoon chopped fresh parsley
1 tablespoon chopped fresh chives

1. In a saucepan add olive oil, garlic and onions. Sauté for 2 minutes.
2. Add tomatoes, vegetable broth, corn, bell peppers, jalapeño, lemon zest, salt, black pepper, apple cider vinegar and bring to a boil.
3. Remove from heat and place soup in the food processor along with basil, parsley and chives blend for 30 seconds to 1 minute.

Mushroom Gravy

A tasty and versatile sauce, this gravy is great served over whole grains, nut loaf, poultry or fish.

1 medium yellow onion, chopped
1-2 teaspoons extra virgin olive oil
1 1/2 cups chopped mushrooms
3 garlic cloves, minced
1/2-1 teaspoon sea salt
1/2 teaspoon crushed black pepper (if you like spicy add up to 1 teaspoon)
1 teaspoon turmeric
1 cup vegetable broth
2 teaspoons arrowroot (you can substitute corn starch or wheat flour depending on your pantry)

1. Heat olive oil on medium high and add onions, salt and pepper.
2. Cook for 2 minutes or until the onions become translucent.
3. Reduce heat to medium-low and add garlic, mushrooms and turmeric. Cook until mushrooms are soft.
4. In a small bowl mix the flour and broth until well combined.
5. Slowly pour the broth and flour mix into the pan, and stir until gravy thickens, about 4-5 minutes.

Savory Sweet Potatoes

Sweet potatoes are a 'superfood' alternative to white potatoes. They are a wonderful source of fiber and beta carotene which helps support cell renewal.

2 small-medium sweet potatoes
2 cloves garlic, crushed
1 small yellow onion
2 tablespoons extra virgin olive oil
1/2 teaspoon sea salt
1/4 teaspoon pepper

1. Wash the sweet potatoes with a vegetable brush and set aside.
2. Set the food processor with the julienne fixture.
3. Julienne the sweet potatoes in the food processor and remove to a separate bowl. If you don't have a food processor just grate the sweet potatoes.
4. Repeat the same procedure for the onions.
5. In a medium saucepan, add the oil, salt, pepper, garlic and onions and sauté for 2 minutes.
6. Add sweet potatoes and gently stir to make sure they are coated with oil.
7. Continue cooking until sweet potatoes are tender, about 5 minutes.

Minty Summer Squash

This recipe is superb with fresh mint, so make it in the summer when fresh mint is abundant.

2 summer squash
1/2 teaspoon sea salt
1 tablespoon extra virgin olive oil
2 cloves garlic, chopped
2 tablespoons fresh spearmint, minced
Freshly ground black pepper to taste

1. Cut off the bottoms and the stems of the squash. Cut the squash lengthwise into small pieces, about 1/8-inch wide.
2. Sprinkle squash with salt and let stand for 15 minutes.
3. Gently squeeze the squash to release the excess water.
4. In a medium sauté pan, add the olive oil and garlic and sauté for about 1 minute.
5. Add spearmint and the drained squash and cook for another minute. Serve immediately.

Vegetarian Collard Greens

The lemon juice and vinegar in this dish take the bitterness out of the collard greens.

1 bunch fresh collard greens
2 tablespoons extra virgin olive oil
Sea salt and pepper to taste
1 medium yellow onion, chopped
6-8 cloves of garlic, crushed
1 cup vegetable broth
Juice of 1/2 lemon
2-3 tablespoons rice wine vinegar
Pinch of cayenne pepper (optional)

1. Clean the collard greens and strip them from the stalk.
2. Stack 5 or 6 leaves on top of one another and roll them up so they look like a green cigar. Cut across the cigar to make thin strips.
3. In a large pot, over medium heat, add the olive oil, salt, pepper and chopped onions. Sauté until onions are translucent.
4. Add garlic, collard greens and vegetable broth. If you are adding cayenne pepper add it now.
5. Simmer on medium-low head for 30 minutes, stirring occasionally to make sure that the greens are cooking evenly.
6. Add lemon juice and vinegar, and cook for another 15-20 minutes or until greens are tender.

Sautéed Cabbage

Cabbage is full of glutamine which is supportive for healing the digestive tract. This simple recipe goes so well with so many dishes it is worth the experimentation to find your favorite combination.

1 teaspoon of extra virgin olive oil
1 head of cabbage, shredded
4 cloves of garlic, minced
2 teaspoons white wine vinegar
1/2 cup vegetable broth
1 teaspoon chopped chives
1/2 teaspoon cumin

1. In a large skillet sauté cabbage in oil for 3 minutes.
2. Add garlic, water, vegetable broth, vinegar, chives and cumin.
3. Cook covered for 10-15 minutes.

Steamed Broccoli

Broccoli is one of the vegetables that is a good source of calcium. It is also one of greens that children will eat because it reminds them of trees. Make vegetables fun and children are more likely to try them.

1/2 cup water
1 bunch broccoli, stemmed and chopped
2 tablespoons extra virgin olive oil
Juice of 1 lemon, freshly squeezed
1/4 teaspoon sea salt

1. Pour water in the bottom of the pan.
2. Place steamer on the bottom of the pan. Place broccoli on the steamer. If you don't have a steamer then just put the broccoli in with the water. Cover the pan
3. Over medium-low heat, steam for 5-7 minutes until you can pierce the broccoli easily.
4. Put on plate and sprinkle lemon and olive oil over top and serve.

Sweet Sautéed Kale

Kale has one of the highest levels of calcium of any green leafy vegetable. So enjoy kale and get your calcium, too.

1 bunch of kale, washed
1/2 cup chopped yellow onions
2 tablespoons extra virgin olive oil
4 garlic cloves, chopped
Pinch of sea salt
Pinch of black pepper
2 tablespoons balsamic vinegar

1. De-rib kale and tear into bite-sized pieces.
2. In a sauce pan add oil and onions and garlic. Cook for 1 minute.
3. Add kale, salt and pepper. Cook for 4 minutes.
4. Turn off the heat and pour vinegar over kale.

Basic Brussels Sprouts

Cutting the Brussels sprouts into thin slices helps speed up the cooking time and ensure tender sprouts.

1 pound Brussels sprouts
1 tablespoon unsalted butter
1 tablespoon extra virgin olive oil
2 large shallots, thinly sliced
2 teaspoons fresh lime juice
1 teaspoon dill leaves, chopped
Sea salt and pepper to taste

1. Rinse Brussels sprouts and remove discolored leaves.
2. Cut sprouts in half and thinly slice lengthwise.
2. Melt butter with olive oil in a heavy skillet over medium high heat.
3. Add sprouts and shallots and stir-fry until tender and lightly browned, about 8 minutes.
4. Remove from heat and transfer to a large bowl.
5. Drizzle with fresh lime juice, season with sea salt, dill, and pepper, and toss.

Fruit-Filled Acorn Squash

Many people are uncomfortable using butter because they think it is bad for them. While it is a saturated fat, if you are using it sparingly, i.e. once or twice per week using only one teaspoon to one tablespoon, it will not be harmful to your health. This is a great recipe to start adding squash to your diet. Use it as a side or dessert.

2 acorn squash
2 apples, peeled, cored and diced
1 pear, peeled, cored and diced
1/4 cup raisins
1/ cup orange juice
1 tablespoon turbinado sugar or agave nectar
1/2 teaspoon cinnamon
1/4 teaspoon nutmeg
2 tablespoons sunflower oil or 1 tablespoon butter
Mint sprigs

1. Preheat the oven to 325°F.
2. Cut the acorn squash into halves and remove the seeds. Pour 1/4 cup of water into a baking dish and place squash cut-side down. Bake for 45 minutes or until tender. Remove the squash from the baking dish and pierce with a fork in several places. Let cool slightly while preparing the filling.
2. In a bowl combine apples, pears, raisins, turbinado sugar, cinnamon and nutmeg.
3. Place vegetable oil or butter in a saucepan. Add the ingredients from the bowl and cook uncovered for about 5 minutes using medium heat.
4. Add orange juice and cook until the ingredients are soft, about 5 minutes. Remove from heat.
5. Spoon some of the juice into the warm squash, and add about 1/4 cup of filling.
6. Finish with a sprig of mint and serve.
* To make blood sugar balancing use agave nectar not sugar.

Zucchini Pizza

This tasty snack will satisfy your pizza cravings and add fiber to your snack time. Zucchini should be crisp.

2 zucchini, sliced about 1/4 inch thick
1/2 cup tomato sauce or pizza sauce
1/2 cup sliced pitted black olives
1/2 cup minced green onions
½ cup grated fresh mozzarella

1. Preheat oven to 350°F.
2. Line up slices of zucchini on a cookie sheet.
3. Spread the tomato sauce on top of the zucchini.
4. Sprinkle on olives, onion, and mozzarella.
5. Place on a baking sheet and bake until cheese is melted and bubbly, 8-11 minutes.

Candied Apple Sweet Potatoes

This is a healthy spin on an old favorite. It's delicious and perfect for those chilly fall days.

2 pounds small sweet potatoes, peeled
1 1/2 cups apple cider
1 teaspoon powdered ginger
1 tablespoon cinnamon
1 teaspoon nutmeg
1/4 cup turbinado sugar

1. Preheat the oven to 375 °F.
2. Slice the sweet potatoes being careful not too cut them too thin or you'll dilute the flavor and richness of the dish. Aim for 1/4" thickness. If you have a food processor, it can save you time and muscle aches.
3. Arrange the sliced sweet potatoes in layers at the bottom of a greased baking dish.
4. In a small bowl, mix the cider, ginger, cinnamon and nutmeg. Pour this over the potatoes.
5. If the liquid does not cover the potatoes, add water until the potatoes are covered.
6. Sprinkle the turbinado sugar over the top of the potatoes.
7. Occasionally open the oven, pull out the sweet potatoes and stir the mixture so the spices mix well with the sweet potatoes. Do this at least twice.
8. Cook for 50 minutes or until the liquid has softened and tenderized the sweet potatoes.

Curried Mixed Greens

I created this curry to get a combination of vegetables and protein that I could put inside of West Indian roti. Roti is similar to a tortilla but it thinner and made with chickpea flour instead of wheat.

1 1/2 cup vegetable broth
1 small red onion, diced
2 roasted red peppers, diced
6 garlic cloves, minced
4-5 large leaves of collards greens, cleaned and cut into strips
4-5 large leaves of turnip greens, cleaned and cut into strips
4-5 large leaves of mustard greens, cleaned and cut into strips
3 cups of spinach, cleaned and cut into strips
2 tablespoons curry powder
1 teaspoon sea salt
1/4 teaspoon black pepper
1 cup diced potatoes
2 cups cooked chickpeas,(may use canned) cooked

1. Add 1/4 cup of the vegetable broth, red onions, red peppers and garlic to a large sauté pan, and boil at low heat for 5 minutes, until soft.
2. Add the greens, curry powder, salt, pepper, potatoes and the rest of the vegetable broth.
3. Cook for 20 minutes or until potatoes are soft.
4. Add cooked chickpeas and cook for 5 minutes to warm the chickpeas.

Veggies with Pesto

Veggies with Pesto is an excellent summer dish. It goes well with the Nutty Rice with Mushrooms, or another whole grain dish.

1 cup fresh basil leaves
1 tablespoon pine nuts
3 tablespoons extra virgin olive oil
1 tablespoon water
1 garlic clove
1/4 cup cooked white beans (may use canned)
1/4 teaspoon sea salt
2 tablespoons extra virgin olive oil
1 carrot, peeled and cut into strips
1 medium zucchini, sliced
1 cup sliced eggplant
1/2 cup sliced red onion
1/2 cup sliced bell pepper
1/4 teaspoon black pepper

1. Pesto: Place basil, pine nuts, oil, water, garlic, white beans, salt and pepper in a blender and blend for 45 seconds or until creamy.
2. In a saucepan over medium heat, add olive oil, salt and pepper. Add carrots, zucchini, eggplant, onion and bell peppers.
3. Sauté for 5-8 minutes.
4. Remove from heat and toss with pesto.
5. Serve warm or room temperature.

Sweet Swiss Chard

Be careful not to overcook the chard. It will be bright green and shiny when it's finished.

1 bunch Swiss chard
2 teaspoons extra virgin olive oil
6 cloves garlic, minced
1/2 cup chopped red onion
1/2 cup chopped yellow bell pepper

1. De-vain the Swiss chard by pulling the leaves from the stem. Tear the leaves into bite-sized pieces and place them in a large bowl filled with cold water. This will wash dirt from the leaves and help it wilt during cooking.
2. In a sauté pan on medium-low heat, add oil, garlic, red onions and yellow peppers. Sauté for 1 minute.
3. Add the Swiss chard and cook for another 3-4 minutes, turning the chard until it wilts.

* To make anti-inflammatory or elimination delete bell pepper.

Sweet Potato Stir-Fry

To make this recipe vegetarian, be sure to find the vegetarian Worchester sauce in your grocery store.

3 teaspoon extra virgin olive oil
1 small sweet potato, diced
3 cloves garlic, chopped
1 small onion, chopped
1 teaspoon fresh ginger, minced or grated
1/2 cup chopped zucchini
1/2 cup chopped celery
1 cup chopped baby bok choy
1 1/2 cup black beans, cooked (or one15-ounce can)
2 teaspoons tamari or soy sauce
1 teaspoon Worchester sauce

1. In a large sauce pan, add oil, sweet potato, garlic, onion and ginger, and sauté for 12 minutes.
2. Add zucchini, celery, bok choy and black beans and cook or another 7 minutes or until sweet potato are soft.
3. Remove from the heat and stir in tamari and Worchester sauce.

Curried Chard and Potatoes

I substituted spinach instead of the chard and it was just as enjoyable. So play with substituting greens and vegetables.

4 leaves red or white chard, both stems and leaves
2-4 cups water
2 medium red-skinned potatoes, washed and cubed
1 2/3 cups water
1 1/2 teaspoons curry powder
1/2 teaspoon ground coriander
1/2 teaspoon ground cumin
5 garlic cloves, minced
1 teaspoon sea salt
1/2 teaspoon black pepper
1/4 teaspoon cayenne pepper

1. Wash the chard leaves and stems. Remove stems and chop. Tear leaves into bite-sized pieces and set aside.
2. In a large sauté pan, add potatoes and enough water to cover potatoes. Bring to a low boil and cook for 20 minutes.
3. Once the potatoes are tender, add the curry powder, coriander, cumin, garlic, salt, black pepper and cayenne pepper and stems of chard and cook for 5 minutes.
4. Add the chard leaves and cook for another 5 minutes.

Vegetarian Lettuce Wraps

This recipe makes a filling main dish. If you can't find bean thread noodles then substitute thin rice noodles. These can be found in the international section of most stores.

1/4 cup natural peanut butter
2 tablespoons tamari
1/4 cup honey
Juice of 1 lime
1 teaspoon chili powder
1/2 package of bean thread noodles
1 tablespoon sesame oil
1/2 cup minced red onions
1/2 cup shredded carrot
1/2 cup chopped celery
1 cup chopped bok choy or your favorite cabbage
1/2 cup chopped peanuts (or any roasted nuts)
1 head lettuce separated and washed (Romaine, Boston, etc.)
1/2 cup chopped fresh cilantro
1/4 cup chopped scallions
1 lime, sliced into wedges

1. Cook the noodles according to package directions. While the noodles are cooking, make dressing in a small bowl by combining peanut butter, tamari, honey, lime and chili.
2. Heat sesame oil in a saucepan over medium-low heat. Add onion, carrots, celery, and bok choy. Cook for 4 minutes.
3. Add noodles and peanuts and mix well. Remove from heat.
4. Add dressing to the mixture.
5. Take a lettuce leaf and add a spoonful of filling. Top with scallions and cilantro.
6. Squeeze lime juice over lettuce filling and serve.

Spaghetti Squash Pasta

This is a squash that when cooked correctly looks like pieces of spaghetti. The cooking process is different based on the size of squash that you choose. My suggestion is that you choose the smallest one that you can find because they yield more than you might think.

1 medium spaghetti squash

1. Puncture holes in the squash with a knife, making sure to evenly distribute holes over the entire squash.
2. Microwave instructions: Place in the microwave on high for 15 minutes, turning every 5 minutes to ensure even cooking. Take the squash out of the microwave with oven mitts, it will be hot! Oven instructions: Place squash on a cookie sheet and in the oven at 350 °F for 45-60 minutes or until soft.
3. Let the squash cool for 10 minutes. Cut the squash in half.
4. Scoop out the seeds and discard.
5. Scoop out the meat of the squash. It will start to unravel into strings like spaghetti.
6. Top with the Tomato Basil Sauce or your favorite spaghetti sauce.

Tomato Basil Sauce

This simple sauce is a great base sauce. You can add your favorite ingredients to make this fantastically great for your taste buds.

6 quarts water
6 medium tomatoes
3 tablespoons extra virgin olive oil
3 cloves of garlic, chopped
1/3 cup chopped fresh parsley
1/3 cup chopped fresh basil
2 tablespoon dried oregano
1/4 teaspoon of sea salt
1/4 teaspoon of pepper

1. Bring water to a boil in a large pot with 1 teaspoon of salt.
2. Carefully drop the tomatoes into the water for 15-30 seconds.
3. Scoop them out and run under cold water. Remove the skin, which should peel off with ease.
4. Cut tomatoes into chunks and set aside.
5. Heat olive oil in a saucepan over medium heat. Add garlic and cook for a 2 minutes. Add parsley, basil, oregano, salt and pepper.
6. Add tomatoes and cook for 20-30 minutes. You want the sauce to thicken.

Bella Burgers

Portobello mushrooms are a refreshing change from meat or grain burgers. Marinating the portobellos gives them a smooth flavor and makes you feel like you are having a satisfying sandwich.

3 large portobello mushrooms
6 garlic cloves
2 tablespoons balsamic vinegar
1/4 cup extra virgin olive oil
1/8 teaspoon black pepper
1/2 cup chopped lettuce
1/4 cup chopped fresh chives
1/2 cup sliced tomatoes (optional)
4 teaspoons of Dijon mustard
1/2 cup sliced red onions
4 whole grain buns or gluten free bread or whole wheat tortillas

1. In a medium bowl, add garlic, balsamic vinegar, and pepper. Marinate the mushrooms in this mixture for at least 1 hour.
2. In a saucepan, add the red onions and olive oil and sauté for 2 minutes.
3. Add portobello mushrooms and cook until soft, about 5-8 minutes.
4. Serve on a whole grain bun with sliced tomatoes, lettuce and mustard.

Eggplant Casserole

This is a hearty meal that is focused on vegetables. If you double the recipe you could serve it like a lasagna using the eggplant instead of noodles.

3/4 cup raw almonds
2 tablespoon Italian seasoning
1/2 teaspoon black pepper
1/2 teaspoon sea salt
1 cup water
1 large eggplant, sliced into 1/8-inch disks
2 tablespoons extra virgin olive oil
1 cup diced yellow onion
4 cups chopped fresh spinach
1 1/2 cups cooked canellini beans (may use canned)
1 teaspoon Italian seasonings
1 cup Tomato Basil Sauce or your favorite tomato sauce
1 cup mozzarella cheese

1. Place almonds in a blender and grind to a fine powder.
2. Mix almond crumbs, Italian seasoning, pepper and salt.
3. Dip eggplant slices into water. Spoon almond crumbs on both sides.
4. In a saucepan heat the oil and gently sauté the eggplant for 2 minutes on each side or until tender. Remove from the heat and place on paper towels to remove excess oil. Complete all the pieces of eggplant.
5. Preheat the oven to 350 °F.
6. In the bottom of a casserole pan layer the eggplant to cover the bottom.
7. In a saucepan, sauté oil, onions, spinach, beans, and Italian seasoning for 3 minutes. Then, pour the spinach mixture over the eggplant discs.
8. Add the tomato sauce and grated cheese. Bake for 20 minutes.

Eggplant Envelopes

This along with the hummus half-moon pies are great ways to get veggies into your kids or adults without them really knowing it. Using leftover tomato sauce allows you to recycle sauce and skip mayo all together. Yet another example of changing up flavors using vegetables.

1 baby eggplant
1 teaspoon sea salt
1 tablespoon black pepper
2 tablespoons Italian seasoning
1 tablespoon extra virgin olive oil
2 cloves garlic, minced
4 whole wheat tortillas
1 cup tomato sauce (Tomato Basil or your favorite)
1 cup roasted red pepper slices (optional)
2 cups chopped romaine lettuce

1. Cut off the ends of the eggplant, and thinly slice lengthwise (approximately 1/8 inch). Season the eggplant with salt, pepper and Italian seasoning.
2. In a saucepan, add olive oil and garlic and cook on medium-low heat for 1 minute.
3. Add eggplant to the pan and sauté until soft (translucent in color), approximately 4 minutes.
4. Warm the tortilla in the oven for 1 minute.
5. Place the tortilla on a plate and spread with 1 tablespoon of tomato sauce.
6. Place a couple of roasted red pepper slices and 1/4 cup of romaine lettuce on the tortilla.
7. Finally, add 3-4 slices of eggplant on top of the lettuce.
8. Roll the tortilla away from you until it looks like a burrito. Repeat for all tortillas, and serve.

Sweet Things

Avocado Mid-Day Delight

Avocado is a great source of essential fatty acids, especially Omega 6, and fiber. Good fats are important for the proper functioning of male, female and stress hormones.

1/4 cup fresh mashed avocado
1/2 cup rice milk or other milk substitute
1 teaspoon honey
1/2 frozen banana
1/2 cup frozen mango pieces
1/4 cup frozen peaches
1/4 cup apple juice

1. In a blender whip together avocado and milk.
2. Add honey, banana, mango and peach pieces. Whip another 10 seconds or until smooth.
3. Add apple juice and mix 5 seconds.
4. Freeze leftover smoothie. (To reuse, defrost for about 10 minutes, then place in blender for 40 seconds.)

Oatmeal Smoothie

I created this smoothie when one of my personal trainer friends asked for a pre-workout drink. Enjoy!

1/2 cup oatmeal, cooked
1 cup rice milk
1/2 banana, peeled
1-2 teaspoons black strap molasses
1/2 teaspoon vanilla extract
1/4-1/2 teaspoon cinnamon

Add all ingredients to a blender and combine until smooth, about 1 minute.

Almond Smoothie

Be open to creating smoothies that have proteins and good fats. Keeping the almonds whole while you blend adds fiber.

1/2 cup coconut milk
1 cup water
1/2 cup almonds
1/2-1 teaspoon almond extract
1 teaspoon honey

Add all ingredients to a blender and combine until smooth, about 1 minute.

Old-Fashioned Apple Pie

Fruit pies are always a more nutrient dessert option than cakes, pastries or cookies. It is important to be mindful about adding fiber to the diet whenever possible.

5 Granny Smith apples, cored, peeled and sliced
Zest of 1 lemon
2 tablespoons of lemon juice
1/2 cup turbinado sugar
2 tablespoon unbleached flour
1 teaspoons ground cinnamon
1/2 teaspoon grated nutmeg
1/2 teaspoon ground cloves
1 pre-made non-hydrogenated pie crust

1. Preheat oven to 400 °F.
2. In a large bowl, combine all of the ingredients.
3. Lower the oven temperature to 375 °F, place the pie in the oven and bake for 45 minutes.

Berry Pear Pie

Hydrogenated oils or trans fatty acids are harmful to the body because they cannot be processed well in our body. Whenever you purchase pie crust or baked goods check the package to make sure you are not buying them.

3 medium Anjou or Bartlett pears, seeded, peeled and sliced
1/2 cup fresh cranberries
1 cup turbinado sugar
1 heaping tablespoon flour
1 teaspoon ground cinnamon
1/4 teaspoon ground ginger
1/4 teaspoon sea salt
1/2 cup orange juice
2 teaspoons grated orange zest
1 pre-made non-hydrogenated pie crust

1. Preheat oven to 425°F.
2. In a large bowl, add pears, cranberries, sugar, flour, cinnamon, ginger, salt, orange juice and zest. Mix and pour into the pie crust.
3. Bake for 15 minutes, and then lower the heat to 350 °F and bake 30 minutes until pie is golden brown.

Apple Crisp

You can substitute berries, pears, peaches or plums in this basic crisp recipe depending on what's fresh and in season.

6 Granny Smith apples, washed, peeled, sliced
1 tablespoon fresh lemon juice
2 teaspoons ground cinnamon
1 teaspoon ground cardamom
1/3 cup frozen apple juice concentrate, thawed
1 teaspoon safflower oil
1 1/2 cups your favorite granola

1. Preheat oven to 350 °F.
2. In a large bowl placed sliced apples, lemon juice, cinnamon, cardamom and apple juice.
3. Mix gently so you don't crush the apples.
4. Lightly grease a casserole or pie pan and pour apples into the dish.
5. Bake for 30 minutes.
6. Remove from the oven. Sprinkle the granola over the apple and bake for another 15-20 minutes until the apples are bubbling.
7. Remove and let cool for 10 minutes.

Getting Pumpkin or Squash Meat

Simple instructions to get the meat out of the squash in your favorite recipes.

Three Ways to Get the Meat Out of a Pumpkin/Squash:

On the stove: Place the pumpkin/squash in a pan of water on medium heat. Cook for 30-60 minutes or until the skin can be pierced easily with a knife.

In the oven: Put several holes in the skin of the pumpkin/squash. Heat oven to 400 °F and bake for 50 -60 minutes or until the skin can be pierced easily with a knife.

In the microwave: Place the pumpkin/squash in a microwave safe dish. Pierce with a knife to make several holes in the skin. Heat on high for 7- 10 minutes or until the skin can be pierced by a knife easily.

Once the pumpkin has been softened, scoop out the seeds and throw them away or save them to roast in the oven. Then scoop out the meat of the pumpkin and use for a variety of dishes, like the Pumpkin Bread, Acorn Squash with Fruit Filling or turkey stuffing.

Kabocha Squash Pie

I decided to use a kabocha squash for this pie just because I was at the farmers' market and saw a beautiful orange variety (some varieties are dark green). You might decide to try another squash like butternut, or acorn. The point is-experiment with squash!

1 kabocha squash
1/3 cup coconut milk or lite coconut milk depending on preference
1 teaspoon vanilla extract
1 teaspoon ground allspice
1/2 cup maple syrup
1 egg or egg substitute equal to one egg
1 1/2 cup raw pecans
1/2 cup turbinado sugar

1. Pierce holes in the kabocha squash and place on a cookie sheet for about 50 minutes in the oven at 375 °F. Take out of the oven and let cool.
2. Reduce oven temperature to 350 °F. Once cool, peel off the outside of the squash. Cut in half and scoop out the seeds to the trash.
3. Scoop out the inner flesh and set aside. Consider freezing unused portion for next time.
4. To make the crust: In a blender or food processor break pecans into a course meal.
5. Add turbinado sugar and pulse 5-10 times.
6. Remove from appliance and use mixture to cover the bottom of the pie plate.
7. Cook in the oven for 10 minutes at 300 °F.
8. In the food processor, add 3 cups of kabocha squash, coconut milk, vanilla, ground allspice, maple syrup and egg or egg substitute. Blend for 45 seconds.
9. Pour into the crust and bake for 50 minutes or until firm.

Sweet Potato Pie

This dish is great as a pie, but it's also delicious as a pudding with no crust at all. You can also use the crust from the Kabocha Squash Pie recipe.

4-6 small-medium sweet potatoes, rinsed
1 organic egg or egg substitute equal to 1 egg
1/4 cup turbinado sugar
1 teaspoon cinnamon
1 teaspoon nutmeg
1/4 teaspoon allspice
1/4 teaspoon sea salt
1/4 cup milk or milk substitute (rice milk adds sweetness)
Pre-made, organic pie crust with no hydrogenated oils

1. Preheat the oven to 400 °F.
2. With a sharp knife, pierce the sweet potatoes several times. Bake on a cookie sheet for 45 minutes or until soft.
3. Let the sweet potatoes cool to the touch and then peel the skin off. The skin should easily fall off the meat of the potato.
4. Turn the oven up to 375 °F.
5. Place skinned potatoes in a bowl or food processor, and add eggs, sugar, cinnamon, nutmeg, allspice, salt and milk. Mix for 2 minutes.
6. Pour into a pie crust and bake for 50-60minutes or until firm.

Pumpkin Bread

This is a good transition recipe if you are used to eating cakes and pastries. The pumpkin and whole wheat flour introduce fiber into your sweet palate.

6 tablespoons butter or vegan butter substitute
2/3 cups turbinado sugar
2 organic eggs or egg substitute equal to 2 eggs
1 cup mashed pumpkin (see instructions for 'Getting Pumpkin or Squash Meat')
1 teaspoon vanilla extract
3/4 cup whole wheat flour
3/4 cup unbleached flour
1 teaspoon baking soda
1 teaspoon ground ginger
1/2 teaspoon ground nutmeg
1/2 teaspoon ground allspice
1/4 teaspoon baking powder
1/3–1/2 cup milk or milk substitute

1. Preheat oven to 350 °F.
2. In a large bowl add the butter or vegan butter substitute and turbinado sugar, eggs, pumpkin and vanilla. Mix for 1-2 minutes.
3. In another bowl, mix the dry ingredients: whole wheat flour, unbleached flour, baking soda, ground ginger, ground nutmeg, ground allspice and baking powder.
4. Slowly stir the dry ingredients into the wet ingredients. Once all of the ingredients have been combined add the milk or milk substitute.
5. Pour the batter into the loaf pan and bake for 55-65 minutes or until a toothpick stuck in the middle comes out clean.

Poached Pears

Pears are a great fall fruit. This is an easy recipe that is fancy and will satisfy your taste buds while increasing your servings of fruits and vegetables.

3 pears, halved, seeded and peeled
4 cups water
1 lemon, squeezed
1 teaspoon vanilla extract
1 teaspoon cinnamon
2 teaspoons maple syrup

1. In a 4-quart pan add water and bring to a boil.
2. Add pears and cook for 8-10 minutes or until tender. Remove to cool.
3. Pierce pears in several places for syrup.
4. In a small bowl mix lemon juice, vanilla, cinnamon and maple syrup.
5. Pour over pears.

Food Lifestyles

Introduction to Food Lifestyles

Why did I choose these Food Lifestyles? These are the plans that are used most in my practice. I share them to help you understand that in order to achieve the health that you desire you will have to commit to a lifestyle change that includes food.

These are not fad diets. These are changes that will improve your quality of life if you are willing to invest the time that it takes to form a new habit. The largest requirement is the commitment you make to yourself to take the time to learn new patterns revolving around food. The rest will fall into place.

How do I choose the best Food Lifestyle for my patients? I use the underlying principles outlined in the Food Lifestyles to understand what is happening inside their bodies. Once we observe and understand the core problems, we use food as our medicine to support the body's innate ability to help itself – the basic principle of naturopathic medicine.

Whenever possible I will recommend that you use foods that are pesticide and hormone free-- in other words, organic. Eating organic foods reduces the toxic load on the body. If you can't buy everything organic, try to avoid 'the dirty dozen', the Environmental Working Group's list of the top twelve conventionally grown fruits and vegetables most heavily laden with pesticides: peaches, apples, sweet bell peppers, celery, nectarines, strawberries, cherries, lettuce, imported grapes, pears, spinach and potatoes. Buy these organic whenever you can. (For the complete list, see www.ewg.org)

You will notice that some health conditions appear under more than one Food Lifestyle. Medicine is both an art and a science, so there is always more than one approach to health problems. I would recommend that if you are having a health challenge and you want to use this book as a guide, you also consult a qualified licensed naturopathic physician to help you decide the best Food Lifestyle and treatment plan for your needs. If you don't know how to find a naturopathic physician, you can always contact my office at www.healthydaes.org and we can assist you, or you can go to www.naturopathic.org to locate a naturopathic physician in your area.

Anti-Inflammatory Food Lifestyle

Inflammation occurs when there is damage to a cell or organ in the body. In its short term or acute phase it is part of the normal repair process categorized by redness, pain, swelling and heat. The immune system responds by releasing chemical signals in the damaged area to begin and complete the healing process. When there is long term inflammation, instead of creating healing, the chemical messengers and the immune system actually *cause* tissue damage and destruction. A pathway of destructive hormones in the prostaglandins cascade causes the tearing down of tissue and makes the tissue less able to heal. This results in increases in inflammation, mucus production, clotting of blood cell platelets, and swelling. This can happen in many parts of the body, from the joints to the blood vessels. Over time this inflammation can cause major health challenges like high blood pressure, heart disease and joint destruction.

There are other prostaglandin pathways that reduce tissue destruction. These actually support the immune systems ability to heal from acute and chronic inflammation. One of the best ways to shift the body into these healing pathways is through the foods that you eat. Drinking water is also a crucial part of the anti-inflammatory process. Foods that promote the anti-inflammatory pathway and should be indulged in as much as possible include vegetables of all kinds, whole grains (millet, basmati rice, rye, barley, quinoa, amaranth, spelt, buckwheat, oats, brown rice, wild rice, teff), legumes and beans (split peas, lentils, chickpeas, and kidney, pinto, soy, mung, aduki, and azuki beans), raw nuts and seeds (walnuts, sesame seeds, flaxseeds), fish (especially cold water fish, salmon, halibut, cod, bass, sardines, tuna, mackerel), chicken, turkey, fruits, small amounts of honey or maple syrup, avocados, olives and olive oil, sunflower and safflower oils.

Foods that promote inflammation and should be avoided while on this Food Lifestyle: alcohol, caffeinated beverages, oranges, corn products, eggs, fried foods, milk and dairy products, night shade family fruits and vegetables (bell peppers, tomatoes, eggplant, potatoes – all except for sweet potatoes), peanuts and peanut butter, pork, red meats (that haven't been farmed raised), refined foods, sugar and products with high amounts of sugar, wheat products, and processed foods including frozen foods, pasta, and candy.

Health conditions that have benefited from this type of Food Lifestyle in my practice include: heart disease of any kind, high blood pressure, heart attack, stroke, clogging of the arteries, autoimmune diseases, rheumatoid arthritis, lupus, multiple sclerosis, gastritis, and premenstrual symptoms.

Blood Sugar Balancing Food Lifestyle

Dysglycemia is defined as the inappropriate regulation of blood sugar in the body. Under normal circumstances, the body takes in food and through the process of digestion it turns that food into fuel or glucose. Glucose then enters the blood stream as it makes its way to the cells. One of organs, the pancreas, releases a hormone called insulin in response to the presence of glucose in the blood stream. Insulin binds to the surface of cells and allows the easy passage of glucose from the blood stream into the cell. The amount of insulin released by the pancreas is in direct proportion to the amount of glucose in the blood stream. When there are disruptions in this process, health conditions arise. The most common are hyperglycemia, or diabetes, and hypoglycemia.

Diabetes has become a huge problem in the United States over the past 25 years. Current research estimates that 21 million Americans are affected by this health condition. The most prevalent form is non-insulin dependent diabetes mellitus or type II. In this form, cells are not responding to the insulin that is being released from the pancreas, and the body is becoming insulin resistant. This lack of response causes the amount of glucose circulating in the blood to be constantly higher than normal. Another form is insulin-dependent diabetes mellitus or type I. In type I, the pancreas is no longer able to produce enough insulin, and as a result people suffering from this form must take insulin injections.

On the opposite side of the scale some people have difficulty regulating the amount of insulin that is released in response to normal amounts of glucose in the blood. This is hypoglycemia. This happens when they eat meals that have high amounts of simple carbohydrates, foods that break down into glucose quickly, causing the pancreas to release large amounts of insulin at one time. This in turn causes the glucose to enter into the cells too quickly, and the blood sugar goes from being too high to too low. This can cause jittery feelings, nausea, irritability, hunger, sweatiness, dizziness, anxiety, and more severely, blackout or unconsciousness. You may have experienced a mild case of this if you have ever skipped meals. Someone who has this as a disease process will experience these symptoms frequently or daily.

The fundamentals of a Blood Sugar Balancing Food Lifestyle revolve around eating foods that have a combination of healthy proteins, complex carbohydrates -- especially those with good amounts of insoluble fiber – and small amounts of good fat. This combination helps reduce the amount of insulin required for each meal, and also slows the quantity and amount of glucose that enters the bloodstream.

It is important that people following this diet eliminate refined sugar and processed junk food. I have found that patients that follow this type of diet will have improvements in their daily blood sugar levels within two weeks. Chronic stress will induce insulin resistance, so making behavioral changes to support healthy stress management is an essential part of this Food Lifestyle as well. Lastly, one of the most important changes that is required is to become conscious of recommended portion sizes and satiety levels. Most people eat past the point of being comfortably full without realizing it and this contributes to higher blood sugars.

Health conditions that have benefited from this type of Food Lifestyle in my practice include: diabetes type I., diabetes type II., polycystic ovaries, Polycystic Ovarian Syndrome, reactive hypoglycemia, anxiety, panic attacks, irritability, metabolic syndrome, and Syndrome X (a combination of obesity, hypertension, atherosclerosis and insulin resistance).

Dairy-Free Food Lifestyle

Many people suspect that eating dairy products can cause discomfort in their bodies. This can be due to lactose intolerance or an allergy to dairy products. Dairy products include milk, yogurt, kefir, butter, and cheese.

It has been estimated that about 70% of the world's population is lactose-intolerant. Lactose intolerance means that the body is not, or is no longer, able to produce an enzyme called lactase. Lactase is required to break down a sugar called lactose, which is found in milk, yogurt and other dairy products. This enzyme is present in infants to help digest breast milk (or formula). Lactase decreases production as a child ages and matures to adulthood. Once the body can no longer break down the milk sugar, the symbiotic microorganisms found in the intestinal tract utilize the undigested milk sugar as food, causing symptoms such as gas, bloating, abdominal pain, cramping or diarrhea.

Another type of dairy sensitivity occurs due to an immune response called type IV. hypersensitivity reaction. There is a reaction between the food, the antigen and the immune system antibody. This antigen-antibody reaction can present itself with a variety of symptoms. This reaction is challenging to track because it may appear up to three days after an exposure to dairy products. Because of the difficulty in spotting this reaction, it is important to remove dairy products from the diet for a couple of months to give the immune system time to stop producing an antibody response. After two months, dairy products suspected of causing the reaction can be added back to the diet one at a time to see if each creates any of the previous symptoms.

One question that many people have about taking dairy out of their diet is, "How will I get my daily calcium requirement?" The answer is simpler than you think: eat more servings of green leafy vegetables. Many are high in calcium.

If you have sensitivities to dairy, check food labels for the following: milk, potassium caseinate, whey, calcium caseinate, dried milk solids, caseine, lactoalbumin, cheese, curds, some margarines, butter or lactose.

Health conditions that have benefited from this type of Food Lifestyle in my practice include: eczema, asthma, recurrent ear infections, recurrent sore throats, enlarged tonsils and adenoids, gastritis, heartburn, gas and bloating several times per week, diarrhea, constipation, sinus problems, stuffy nose, and seasonal allergies.

Detoxification Diet

Toxins are present in daily life. Examples of toxins are food allergies, air pollutants, alcohol, chemical toxins, environmental toxins, pesticides, steroids, refined and processed foods, food additives, hydrogenated oils and trans fatty acids. The increase of daily stress, lower density of nutrients in processed foods, low fiber foods, increases in chemical exposures and lack of exercise have all increased the amount of toxins that accumulate in the body. The body can be so overwhelmed with all these toxins that it does not work as well or create the energy and vitality that people want.

Our body has four organs that focus on ridding the body of toxins: the skin, lungs, kidneys, and liver. All of these organs need to be operating properly to achieve and maintain good health. The Detoxification Diet includes foods that are more easily digestible, giving the digestive system a break.

The Detoxification Diet is best done for a specific period of time- -- about 14 to 28 days. During this time it is recommended that you use foods that are organic to further reduce the toxic load on the body. Foods to include during this detoxification process are: whole grains and cereals like millet, oatmeal, brown rice, barley, wild rice, rye, buckwheat, bran, corn and corn meal. Milk substitutes like rice milk, soy milk, oat milk, or almond milk may be used. Proteins like tofu, cold water fish, legumes and beans are best. All fruits and vegetables, organic if possible, are fine. Use good oils sparingly, like extra virgin olive oil, safflower oil, and sesame oil.

Foods to avoid during this time are: all refined and processed foods, canned products, fried foods of all kinds, canned and frozen juices, roasted and salted nuts, pastries, cookies, candy, ice cream, red meats, poultry, eggs, milk, cheese, margarine, hydrogenated oils, trans fatty acids, white rice, wheat products, sugars, artificial sweeteners, alcohol, coffee, soft drinks and dairy products.

Note: I strongly believe that while on this diet there needs to be special attention placed on mental and spiritual detoxification from negative thoughts, stressful events, difficult people and situations. This allows the brain and spirit to release toxic ideas and beliefs at the same time the body is releasing its toxins. This creates an overall balance for the whole system.

After the Detoxification Diet is completed in the specific time period it is a good idea to move to another Food Lifestyle in this book. Consulting your naturopathic physician to help choose the best lifestyle is the most advisable step.

Health conditions that have benefited from this type of diet in my practice include: digestive complaints of any kind, sinus problems, congestion, headaches, migraines, daily fatigue, frequent colds and flu, skin problems, and lung problems.

↖ Elimination Diet

The immune system is responsible for the defense and protection of the body against foreign invaders and harmful substances. Under normal circumstances there is no interaction between the foods we eat and the immune system. However, some individuals experience immune responses resulting from one of two types of food sensitivities: anaphylactic hypersensitivity, or type I., and delayed hypersensitivity, or type IV.

How can food affect the immune system? Approximately 70% of the body's immune system is located in the area of the digestive tract. On every piece of food there are markers that are used to allow the body to recognize each type of food. If the immune system looks at the marker and registers it as a harmful marker, or antigen, it creates antibodies to rid the body of the antigen. If the immune system identifies a marker as a serious threat it responds with an immediate, or anaphylactic, hypersensitivity. This reaction is categorized by symptoms ranging from minor discomfort to death. Such severe food allergies are usually identified in early childhood. Type IV. food sensitivities are more difficult to track, because symptoms can be both varied and delayed – —up to 72 hours after exposure to the food.

During an Elimination Diet, the most common foods causing sensitivities are removed from the diet for a period of two months. This allows the body time to calm the immune response, and translates into reduction or elimination of symptoms. After the two months, foods will be reintroduced one by one. Each time you introduce a new food, wait at least three days to see if any symptoms return. If a symptom returns, then stop that food immediately. Continue eating the foods on the Elimination Diet until the symptoms go away. Once you are feeling good again then you can add the next food back into the diet. This continues until all the foods are successfully added back. Any food that continues to cause an increase in symptoms will be eliminated from the eating plan indefinitely, or until symptoms do not occur when the food is eaten.

Foods to be eliminated are: all grains except rice, dairy products, shellfish, poultry, red meats, pork, soy and all soy products, most nuts, corn, members of the nightshade family (tomatoes, potatoes, peppers, eggplant), dried fruits, strawberries, bananas, apples, citrus, refined sugars, hydrogenated oils, trans fatty acids, coffee, black teas, alcohol, all sodas and sugary drinks, food additives, artificial colors and flavors, preservatives or sweeteners.

Focus on brown or white rice, grazing animals (lamb, ostrich, buffalo), cold water fish, all vegetables, fruits, walnuts, sesame seeds, and all legumes except cashews and soybeans.

Health conditions that have benefited from this type of diet in my practice include: eczema, asthma, recurrent ear infections, recurrent sore throats, enlarged tonsils and adenoids, gastritis, heartburn, gas and bloating, diarrhea, constipation, sinus problems, stuffy nose, seasonal allergies, migraines, headaches, and joint pain.

Liver Enhancing Food Lifestyle

The liver is one of the most dynamic organs in the body. It is responsible for the production and regulation of many hormones. It is an important detoxifier for harmful substances in the body. It creates bile, which is responsible for fat metabolism, and produces most of the cholesterol used in the body. It performs many functions related to carbohydrate metabolism including storage of blood glucose. The liver also makes some amino acids which are the building blocks for proteins, muscle, and the immune system. It also stores vitamins and minerals needed for biochemical reactions in the body.

This Liver Enhancing Food Lifestyle focuses on supporting the liver's ability to conduct all of its functions optimally. The eating plan revolves around high fiber foods. Fiber acts as a broom to help sweep toxins, cholesterol and triglycerides out of the liver and digestive system. This Food Lifestyle includes three to five servings of fruit daily, and two servings of vegetables with each meal. Fruits and vegetables that are especially supportive to the liver are figs, mangos, peaches, papaya, beets, carrots, cauliflower, kale, dandelion greens and mustard greens. Vegetable proteins like beans, tofu, and legumes provide important soluble fiber to the liver. Grains like rice, quinoa and millet increase micronutrient and vitamin stores. Sulfur-containing foods like onion, garlic and eggs are important to healthy liver detoxification pathways. Foods high in essential fatty acids are needed as well, including cold water fish like salmon, cod, halibut, and avocados, nuts and seeds. Of course water is a crucial part of the detoxification process and needs to be a conscious part of the Liver Enhancing Food Lifestyle plan. I recommend people drink one-half their body weight in ounces daily. If you weigh 100 pounds, you need to drink 50 ounces of water daily.

Any toxins like alcohol, harmful chemicals, environmental chemicals and pesticides, steroids, food sensitivities, refined and processed foods, food additives, hydrogenated oils and trans fatty acids should be strictly avoided on this Food Lifestyle. Natural sweeteners should be eliminated or kept to a minimum.

Health conditions that have benefited from this type of Food Lifestyle in my practice include: high cholesterol, gall bladder disease, hormonal irregularities, PMS symptoms, menopausal symptoms, skin conditions, anxiety, frustration, panic attacks, mood swings, and irritability.

V Vegan Food Lifestyle

A vegan vegetarian diet includes no animal products. The reduction of saturated fats from animal products supports the body's restorative and healing process. The phytonutrients and fiber found in a plant- based diet support the lymphatic system, and the immune system's ability to increase health outcomes. This is especially useful in working with cancer or other chronic, energy-depleting health conditions.

It is important on this Food Lifestyle to include sources of protein with each meal and in each day's intake. Plant- based proteins are generally derived from nuts, seeds, legumes and beans. However proteins are also found in low amounts in most whole grains and vegetables.

Whole grains include any grain that has the fiber part of the grain still intact. Examples are steel cut oats, millet, barley, brown rice, wild rice, amaranth, quinoa, couscous, spelt, bran and corn. Fruits are a wonderful source of flavonoids, carotenoids, and antioxidants. The more colorful the foods, the more nutrients are available for your body. Fresh fruits are always best, and small amounts of dried fruit are also acceptable, although they do contain more sugar. Remember to include seasonal and local vegetables in your plan. Green leafy vegetables, summer and winter squash, and root vegetables are just common examples to include.

Note: People choosing to have a vegan lifestyle have to make sure that they are taking a good B12 supplement. Vegetarian food sources do not have significant amounts of B12.

Health conditions that have benefited from this type of Food Lifestyle in my practice include: cancer patients, patients with immune deficiencies, heart disease, blood vessel problems, and high cholesterol.

Gluten-Free Food Lifestyle

Wheat has a protein called gluten which is difficult for some people to digest. This protein acts as an antigen. Some people have reactions between the gluten antigen and the immune system, causing antibodies to be formed. This antigen-antibody reaction can present itself with a variety of symptoms. The reaction is challenging to track because it can appear up to 72 hours after an exposure to wheat. The most common symptoms are skin rashes or hives, gastrointestinal distress, and breathing problems.

Grains containing gluten and gliadin such as rye, couscous, spelt, barley, and oats can cause the same reaction as wheat. This condition is known as Celiac Disease, which can be determined with a simple blood test. People with Celiac will need a strict gluten-free Food Lifestyle not included in this book. For additional information, visit www.celiac.com and www.glutenfreediet.com.

Gluten intolerance or gluten sensitivity is not always positive on a celiac test, so eliminating all gluten from the diet may be necessary to see a reduction of symptoms or may be the best way to discover discover this problem.

For sensitivities to gluten check food labels for the following: wheat, whole wheat, flour, farina, wheat germ, semolina, wheat starch, bran, durum, and gluten. Wheat can be hidden in many other foods like beverages, bread, cereals, pastries, dessert, hamburger mixes, soy sauce and salad dressings.

Health conditions that have benefited from this type of Food Lifestyle in my practice include: Celiac Disease, headaches, sinus problems, allergies, difficulty losing weight, abdominal pain or bloating, rashes and skin conditions.

Whole Foods Lifestyle

A Whole Foods Lifestyle simply refers to eating foods in their natural state. Foods are categorized in three types: proteins, carbohydrates and fats. A Whole Foods Lifestyle revolves around foods that can be recognized coming from or living on the earth at one time. These foods have a high nutrient density, essential and nonessential amino acids, essential fatty acids, phytochemicals, fiber, and micronutrients required for metabolism and restoration.

Proteins, both animal and plant -based, are a requirement for daily nutrition. Meats should be organic, grass-fed or free- range and nitrate-free whenever possible. It is advisable to avoid pork because of the high concentration of toxins in the meat. Red meats should be lean and be limited to once per week. Chicken, turkey or poultry should be lean whenever possible. Eggs from free-range chickens are high in essential fatty acids and don't cause cholesterol problems. Fish are best if they are cold water because they have the most essential fatty acids – cod, flounder, halibut, herring, mackeral, mahi mahi, red snapper, salmon, swordfish, trout, or tuna. Best cooking methods are baked, broiled, or roasted. Good choices among nuts are almonds, pecans, walnuts, and cashews. Eat peanuts and macadamia nuts sparingly. Examples of legumes: pinto beans, navy beans, green peas, string beans, lentils, black-eyed peas, chickpeas (garbanzo beans), lima beans, and soy beans (tofu).

Carbohydrates are composed of grains, vegetables and fruits. Whole grains include any grain that has the fiber part intact. For bread, cereal, and pasta, labels that read "Wheat Flour", "Unbleached Wheat Flour" or "Enriched Wheat Flour" are not acceptable, so be careful. Look for the words "Whole Grain". Other examples of whole grains are steel cut oats, millet, barley, brown rice, wild rice, amaranth, quinoa, couscous, spelt, bran, or corn. Limit grains to two portions per day. Vegetables and fruits are healthy sources of fiber and micronutrients. Eat and enjoy them raw, sautéed, roasted, blanched, or pureed. Eat them in as large portions as possible. Limit dried fruits which can be overly sweet.

Avoid hydrogenated oils and trans fatty acids as they have been implicated in disease-forming processes in the body. The best oils are found in fish, nuts, seeds, and avocados. Olive, safflower, sunflower, walnut and sesame oil are good for cooking. Some oils like flaxseed are good for salad dressing but not for cooking because the boiling point is low. Butter can be used in small portions.

This is the best maintenance Food Lifestyle once health goals have been achieved.

Food Information

The Whole Foods Pantry

Once you have made the commitment to change your eating habits the next step is preparation. Having a well stocked pantry makes cooking a quicker and more pleasurable experience. This list primarily includes non-perishables items that are used frequently when making anything from breakfast foods to stews. Once you get in the swing of cooking new recipes that you enjoy, you will see which items you use most.

My suggestion to make stocking your pantry cost- effective is to choose a couple of recipes you like and buy those ingredients, so you will have them in your home. Then once a week or once a month decide to buy another staple and over time you will start to have a well-stocked pantry. Many communities have health food stores with bulk sections. This is a great way to buy herbs, grains, legumes and dried fruit in smaller qualities and for a cheaper price than at your local grocery store. You might have to make a special trip once a month but it will be worth it to have your favorite recipe staples in your home.

Herbs & Spices – Fresh and/or Dry

Allspice
Basil
Bay leaf
Black pepper
Cayenne pepper
Chives
Cinnamon
Coriander
Cumin
Curry powder
Dill
Garlic
Ginger
Italian seasoning
Mint
Dried mustard
Nutmeg
Oregano
Parsley
Rosemary
Sage
Sea salt
Thyme
Vanilla extract

Nuts

Almonds
Cashews
Pecans
Pine nuts
Walnuts

Grains and Dried Foods

Baking soda
Baking powder
Couscous
Dried cranberries
Dried mushrooms
Lentils, green and pink
Oats

Popcorn
Quinoa
Raisins
Raw sugar (turbinado
Rice – brown, wild rice, long grain
Whole wheat flour
Whole wheat noodles

Oil and Condiments

Apple cider vinegar
Balsamic vinegar
Butter NOT margarine
Extra virgin olive oil
Honey
Maple Syrup
Nut butters – peanut butter, almond butter
Vegetable broth – organic
White wine vinegar

Red wine vinegar
Rice milk, soy milk, almond milk, oat milk
Rice wine vinegar
Safflower or sunflower oil
Sesame oil
Soy sauce or tamari (wheat-free soy sauce)

Perishables

Carrots
Garlic
Hot peppers
Limes/lemons
Mushrooms
Onions

Salad greens
Scallions
Seasonal fruit/vegetables
Sweet potatoes
Tomatoes - fresh
Whole wheat tortillas

Canned goods

Tomato sauce
Tomato paste
Olives
Salmon

Stewed tomatoes
Canned beans – chickpeas, black beans, white beans

Frozen foods

Mixed vegetables
Corn
Fruits – berries, bananas, peaches, pineapple

Spinach
Whole grain breads

Healthy Options: Eating Whole Foods Economically

When I first suggest to my patients that I want them to eat healthy, I often get this look like, I can't afford to eat healthy – -- it 's too expensive. I disagree. People can always start to feed themselves better without breaking the bank.

The first step in changing to a healthy food lifestyle is to change your perception about what is healthy. You can buy healthy options even if they are not organic. Healthy options mean choosing whole foods instead of processed, prepackaged, or refined foods. Whole foods are foods that are found close to their natural state. Beans, nuts, seeds, vegetables, fruits, whole grains, and animal proteins are all examples of whole foods. These can usually be found around the perimeter of the grocery store. Cookies, cakes, frozen pizza, pastas, sugary cereals and the like are not examples of whole foods. Those are usually found in the interior of the store.

Let me give you a financial example. A box of high sugar cereal costs much more than a box of oatmeal (bulk, not individually sized packets). Make the healthy *and* economical choice. Watch for weekly specials on produce, and use your pantry list to choose products that are staples in your home when they are on sale. Bulk sections in health food stores and some larger grocery chains sell grains, cereals, dried beans, nuts, seeds, herbs, and dried fruits. This is a great way to buy items in the quantities that you need and for a price that can fit into your budget. If you have the option to shop at ethnic markets, like Asian or Hispanic markets, you can often find fresh produce for less than at the larger groceries stores.

If you are able to buy a few things organic, I would recommend trying to avoid 'the dirty dozen', the Environmental Working Group's (www.ewg.org) list of the top twelve conventionally grown fruits and vegetables most laden with pesticides: peaches, apples, sweet bell peppers, celery, nectarines, strawberries, cherries, lettuce, imported grapes, pears, spinach and potatoes. Buy these organic whenever you can. Also consider finding your local farmers' market and asking the farmers if they use pesticides. Some smaller farms do not use pesticides but can't call their produce 'organic' because of legal definitions and costs involved. This is a good healthy option that can save money as well. Also, look for half-price bins of slightly bruised produce at health food stores or farmers' markets. You can cut the bruised part off and salvage the rest for your recipes.

One of my favorite cost- effective tricks is to buy seeds or little herb plants from a nursery or farmers' market and grow them to use in the kitchen. You can spend $10.00 for 4 or 5 plants and use them all summer long. Place them in a sunny windowsill, water them regularly, and when you're ready to cook, pinch off what you need. If you have children this is a wonderful teaching tool, and it gets children excited about trying foods that they have watched grow.

Sample Menus

The recipes in this book are very easy to combine into menus that suit your Food Lifestyle. A few examples:

Anti-Inflammatory Food Lifestyle

Honey Mustard Salmon
Wild Rice and beans
Steamed Broccoli
Poached Pears

Comforting Carrot Soup
Tofu Scramble
Basic Brussels Sprouts

Blood Sugar Balancing Food Lifestyle

Rosemary Chicken Kabobs
Black Bean Salsa with Guacamole
Minty Summer Squash

Spaghetti Squash
Tomato Basil Sauce
Salmon with Fresh Chives
Apple Crisp

Dairy-Free Food Lifestyle

Healing Turkey Soup
Sweet Sautéed Kale
Fruit-Filled Acorn Squash

Whole Wheat Pasta Medley
Chicken Lettuce Wraps
Poached Pears

Detoxification Diet

Minty Lentils
Wild Rice with Mushrooms

Tofu Scramble
Sweet Swiss Chard

Elimination Diet

Strawberry Spinach Crunch Salad
Salmon with Fresh Chives
Sautéed Cabbage

Bok Choy Stir Fry
Simply Barley
Marinated Kale & Carrot Salad (exclude the tomatoes)

Liver Enhancing Food Lifestyle

Mixed Curry Vegetables
Simply Barley
Sweet Potato Pie

Bok Choy Stir Fry
Orange Rosemary Salad
Nutty Rice with Mushrooms

Vegan Lifestyle

Nut Loaf
Mushroom Gravy
Curried Chard

Vegetarian Lettuce Wraps
Butternut Squash and Quinoa
Kabocha Squash Pie

Wheat-Free Food Lifestyle

Honey Mustard Salmon
Candied Apple Sweet Potatoes
Fruity Fall Field

Chicken Lettuce Wrap
Mixed Curried Vegetables

Whole Foods Lifestyle

Salmon and Tomato Sauce
Brown Rice with Beans
Strawberry Spinach Crunch

Acorn Squash with Turkey
Sautéed Kale
Apple crisp

Bibliography

Elson M. Haas, MD, *The Detox Diet: A How-To & When-To Guide for Cleansing the Body*. Berkeley, Celestial Arts, 2004.

Elson M. Haas, MD, *Staying Healthy with the Seasons*. Berkeley, Celestial Arts, 2003.

Merck Manual, Merck Research Laboratories, Whitehouse Station, N.J. Copyright © 2006-2007.

Russell B. Marz , *Nutrition from Marz,*. Quiet Lion Press, 2nd edition, 1999.

www.whfoods.com, © 2001-2007 The George Mateljan Foundation

Index

About the Author

Dr. Daemon Jones is an emerging voice in community health and nutrition education. A naturopathic physician in private practice in the Washington, DC area, Dr. Jones is also Director of Community Nutrition and on the faculty of Food As Medicine, an annual professional nutrition training program of the Center for Mind-Body Medicine. She teaches at Smith Farm Center for Healing and the Arts, and gives popular nutrition talks and cooking demonstrations, inspiring her audiences to adopt a colorful, healthy, **Whole Foods Lifestyle**. And her friends are lucky because she can ALWAYS whip up a magically delicious meal on the spur of the moment.